ANTARCTICA:
The Worst Place in the World

ANTARCTICA:

The Worst Place in the World

by ALLYN BAUM

The Macmillan Company, New York

Collier-Macmillan Limited, London

ACKNOWLEDGMENT   The Author would like
to express his appreciation to *The New York Times*
for its kind permission to draw upon material used in
his dispatches to them as well as the photographs he took
on their behalf while on assignment in the Antarctic.

*This book is dedicated to all who have
ever been to the Seventh Continent of
our Earth and all who will ever go. And
gratefully to PLB and SA.*

ANTARCTICA:
The Worst Place in the World

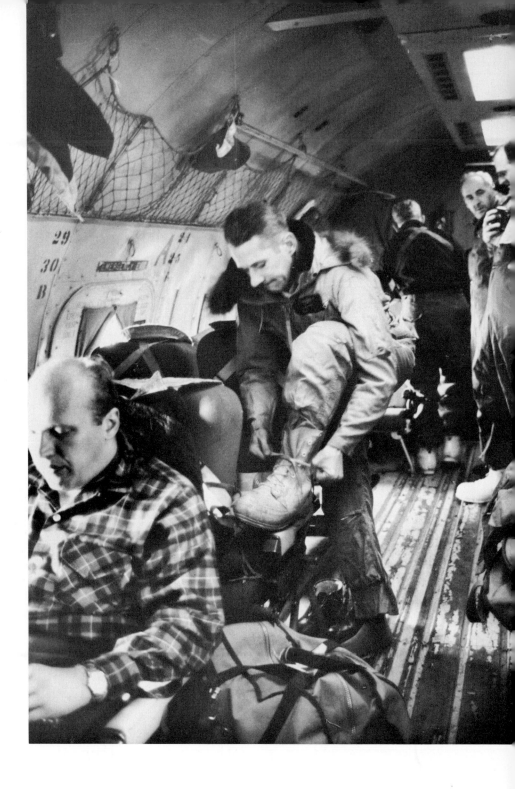

INTRODUCTION

IN A small island of light, surrounded by the gloom of early morning, three men alternately study a weather map and fiddle with the dials of a shortwave radio. Amidst the surging crackle of static, a distant voice emerges from the loudspeaker.

"Hello Deep Freeze HQ . . . Hello Deep Freeze HQ . . . Here is McMurdo with the 3 A. M. weather. Temperature —37° F., winds north northwest at 27 knots, barometric pressure 29.6 rising, ceiling 900 feet in overcast, visibility three miles in blowing snow. Forecast is for winds continuing 27 knots north northwest for next few hours, then backing around to due west and dropping to 10 knots. Temperature expected to rise to —28° F. and ceiling to pick up to 2,300 feet in broken clouds. Prognosis for next 12 hours is good. Over."

The three men in the weather office of Operation Deep Freeze in New Zealand look at one another thoughtfully and then nod. Reaching for the intercom microphone, one of them, a U.S. naval officer, clicks the "on" button and rasps, "Now hear this . . . Now hear this . . . 119, 119 . . . The order is launch—repeat—the order is launch."

Parked on a cement runway of Harewood Airport in warm, civilized Christchurch, New Zealand, is a C-130 Hercules cargo plane. A few mechanics stand idly about under the tall tail of the ugly, snub-nosed plane.

Then the stillness of the airfield is broken by the public address system. The last word of the announcement, "launch," echoes across the deserted runways, and all is scramble. Work lights are switched on around the hangar. Auxiliary power engines cough into action. The plane—long since primed, fueled, and loaded with cargo—becomes the center of scurrying activity. Within moments of the takeoff order, the plane crew dashes across the runway. Passengers, loaded down with heavy green duffel bags full of cold-weather clothing, stumble along toward the aircraft.

The propellers begin to spin and a feeling of unreality grips each passenger as he sleepily buckles himself into one of the uncomfortable canvas-web seats strung along the interior of the plane. Slowly, the passenger begins to realize that, along with tons of supplies, he is part of a priority cargo en route to the blank, bare, freezing white, uninhabited continent of Antarctica.

Every trip to the Antarctic by air is as carefully planned as the most intricate military maneuver. In a way, the flight is a military maneuver, for man is at war with the elements in this area of the world and must fight his way to and from his destination every time he undertakes the trip.

Before each flight is scheduled (several flights a week are made during the five-month antarctic summer), requests for cargo needed by the various U.S. stations in the Antarctic are carefully screened. Only the most urgently needed items are forwarded by air. Even the passengers are listed by priority. Everything else goes by sea.

The countdown involved in an antarctic flight is a seemingly endless affair. The airplane is carefully gone over, almost rivet by rivet; fuel tanks are topped off and the amount carried recorded, down to pints; radio equipment is tested; compasses calibrated; emergency stores counted; and cargo weighed and reweighed as it is logged and loaded aboard.

Weather is checked every thirty minutes, beginning six hours prior to takeoff. Reports from weather stations at the French camp at d'Urville, the Soviet base at Mirny, the Australian station at Wilkes, and the U.S. bases at McMurdo, Pole, Byrd, and Eights are all coordinated and studied by the Deep Freeze weathermen in both New Zealand and Antarctica. This is done to project a favorable and safe forecast for eight hours of flight, with a leeway of two hours in case of adverse winds.

Sometimes these weather reports, while appearing favorable, turn bad after long-range projection. Then the plane, cargo, passengers and crew must wait, sometimes for days, on a standby

The plane keeps in constant touch with base.

alert, until a break in the weather will send through the electrifying order, "Launch!"

The plane, which carries ten tons of cargo in a cavernous fuselage, is equipped with remarkable landing gear—a combination of wheels and skis—which permits it to operate on both airport runways and the snow and ice of the Antarctic. They are flown by the U.S. Navy's VX6 Squadron, an elite, all-volunteer, specially trained, cold-weather outfit that has operated in both the Arctic and Antarctic for many years. Many of the pilots and crews have been flying the New Zealand-Antarctic run for four and five seasons and, though there are few landmarks for them to fly by, they have been over the route so often, they can almost sense their way back and forth like homing pigeons.

The weather forecast for this flight is favorable, so the order is "Launch." As the plane becomes airborne, the passenger's first feeling is great discomfort caused by the high whine of the plane's turbo engines. Since the aircraft is stripped of soundproofing for the sake of weight, the noise is terrifying. Special wax earplugs are issued the passengers to deaden the noise, but they don't help much.

As soon as the plane gains altitude and sets its course, the crew begins checking the plane for cracks in the porthole windows and breaks in the sealing around the cargo door at the back of the plane. The cargo is checked again, and lashed more securely.

Forward in the large cockpit, where seven men can stand comfortably (and two sleep on special bunks), there is a constant chatter over the radio, an exchange of information—weather, course, airspeed, altitude, headwinds, fuel consumption—between the plane and New Zealand and Antarctica. This radio communication will continue, nonstop, until the plane lands safely at its destination.

Meanwhile, behind the pilots, the two navigators begin the continuous computing of plane position. The flight engineer, seated between the pilot and the copilot, steadily flips switches overhead and to either side, smoothing out the engines, all the while juggling figures on fuel consumption. The pilot and co-pilot chat back and forth with one another and with the rest of the crew, checking the plane's performance. Their eyes, ears and instincts must be ever alert to any emergency. There must never be a mistake, however minor. A flight to Antarctica is never routine; it is always high adventure.

Two hours after takeoff, the passengers are advised to change into their thirty pounds of antarctic clothing. Slowly, the cabin temperature begins to drop as the pilot cools the plane to acclimatize the passengers and crew to the cold so that, should the plane be forced down, the cold outside will not come as too great a shock to the body.

Four hours out of New Zealand the point of no return is reached on the eight-hour, twenty-two-hundred mile trip. This is the most vital moment of the flight. After checking with the weather stations in Antarctica and New Zealand, and with his crew as to plane performance and fuel consumption, the pilot must decide whether to go on to McMurdo or turn back to Christchurch. There is no in-between. There are no emergency landing fields on this trip; it's always "go for broke." The decision, based on all the reports, is for McMurdo. The forecast at McMurdo now is for winds of twenty knots, continued blowing snow and a ceiling of fifteen hundred feet in overcast—a marginal forecast. Everyone—pilot, crew and passengers—prays, "The weather better hold."

The first part of the flight is like a gay outing. Passengers and crew banter about why they are going to Antarctica, what they expect to see and what they hope to accomplish. Then, at the point of no return, everyone settles into silence as if by agreement. A sense of apprehension envelops the aircraft. Everyone's thoughts are the same: Will we make it? Why are we here? Why did I come?

Hour after hour, the plane drones on over the vast void of the frozen sea surrounding the continent. Then, suddenly, through the plane's tiny porthole—to the right—there are Cape Adare and the Antarctic. Brown peaks, frosted by snow and tinged gold by the brilliant sun, slam ten thousand feet up from the sea of ice. Every man becomes excited, shaken from his private thoughts to a fever pitch of anticipation. Passengers shoulder one another from the portholes for a view and, perhaps, a picture.

But for the plane crew, it is still all routine. They've seen Cape Adare a dozen times before, perhaps not as clearly as today, but it's an old friend and their first positive navigational marker after six hours of flying. On and on the plane flies. Now the scenery, which previously had been a vast open expanse of white upon white, becomes ever changing. As the plane heads due south, the unbroken plain of sea ice to the left remains flat and featureless as far as the eye can see from thirty thousand feet. But to the right are the glorious peaks of the Admiralty

Range, the Prince Albert Mountains, and the Royal Society Range—the coastline of the Antarctic.

Thirty minutes from McMurdo, the Hercules begins to lose altitude as it nears its destination. Off in the distance, set apart from the other mountain ranges, a solitary white cone pokes up into the blue skies above an overcast of cloud. A gentle white plume wafts from the mountain's top. This is Mount Erebus, 13,200 feet high—the only active volcano yet found in the Antarctic—which stands as the landfall of Ross Island and the site of America's main base at McMurdo Sound.

In clearing skies, the plane slowly circles for its approach to the snow and ice runway that the men of McMurdo have

The first view of Antarctica—Cape Adare. In the background is the Admiralty Range—10,000 feet high.

gouged from the surface of the sea ice surrounding the base. With a crash and a rumble, the plane's skis touch down and, engulfed in a spume of snow kicked up by the whirring props, the plane slithers down the sixty-five-hundred-foot runway to a gradual halt.

As the plane is parked, the doors slide open. You gasp as a —29° F. breath of air crashes in upon your lungs in one short gulp. The sun above is a dazzling fireball; the clouds and overcast have blown away a scant thirty minutes before. The snow is blinding in its glittering glare, even through the heavy dark sunglasses that must be worn to prevent snow blindness. In the distance—thirty, fifty, one hundred miles away—the staggering eleven-thousand- and twelve-thousand-foot needle-tipped peaks of the Royal Society Mountains loom upon the horizon, looking so close you think you can reach them in an hour.

The plane has barely lurched to a halt and the engines stopped turning when a group of featureless, clumsily clad creatures waddle toward the aircraft. They don't look human, but they are. They are surrounded by clouds of vaporized breath. Their beards drip with icicles; their sunglasses glint in the brilliant sun. Their faces are locked in drawn grimaces caused by hours in the cold. You stand looking and gulping in the marrow-chilling cold, but you are ignored. The men rush past to secure the aircraft against the snapping gusts of wind and to unload the sacks of mail just arrived from home. To the men of Mc-Murdo, mail is the most precious and important cargo carried by the planes from New Zealand to Antarctica.

In the midst of all the bustle, a familiar yet alien sound cuts the whipping wind.

"Beep-beep!" Again, "Beep-beep!"

And up grinds an orange Caterpillar tractor with a green radiator on which is written, "We give S&H Green Stamps."

You have arrived in Antarctica . . . the end of the world.

ONE

HIGH above McMurdo Sound, atop a snow-coated, windblown mountain called Observation Hill, stands a large wooden cross. The cross has been blown slightly awry by half a century of buffeting winds, but it still stands as defiantly as the day it was first raised.

Cut into this cross are ten simple words which seem to say all there is to be said about man and his conquest of the Antarctic: "To Seek, to Strive, to Find . . . And Not to Yield." The cross is a memorial, the words a testimonial. Together, they sum up the heroism, the tragedy and the indomitable spirit of all the explorers of the seventh continent of our earth.

Some of these men came to the snows of Antarctica for adventure, others to seek their fortunes. Others still came in the name of science. But each, in some manner, bequeathed to this icebound land a bit of his spirit which continues to haunt the continent, despite the raging winds of time.

The history of the Antarctic is rooted in ancient Greece. As far back as 300 B.C., Greek scholars and philosophers theorized that the earth was round. And because the Greeks loved symmetry, they conceived of the earth as a sphere made up of four continents, each opposite the other, keeping the planet in balance in the heavens.

There is little question the ancient Greeks were aware of snow-covered lands to the far north of their Mediterranean home. With their love of harmony, they believed a similar land, to the south, existed as well. The northern continent was called *Arktos*, which means "The Bear," undoubtedly named for the great constellation of the northern skies we call *Ursa Major*, the "Great Bear." And they envisioned a similar constellation and land, unseen and unknown, directly opposite *Arktos*. This land they called *Antarktos*, or "Opposite Bear."

Over the centuries, man explored and came to know more and more of the world in which he lived. The map makers, drawing and redrawing their maps as new discoveries became known, were more imaginative than accurate and filled in the empty spaces with places that didn't exist. One of these voids was the waters south of Africa. Like the ancient Greeks, the cartographers imagined a great continent to exist in the vicinity of what we now know as Antarctica. They called this land *terra incognita australis*, or "unknown southern land." And *terra incognita australis* it remained until the mid-eighteenth century when Great Britain, disturbed by news of the discoveries of islands in the heretofore deserted South Pacific and Atlantic oceans, felt that if there really were a *terra incognita australis*, England should discover it, claim it, colonize the land and open up a new market for trade.

To undertake these explorations, the Royal Navy chose Captain James Cook to head an expedition to the still uncharted southern waters. He was supplied with two ships, the *Resolution*, with 112 hands, and the *Adventure*, with a crew of 91. Among the stores carried on this first voyage to the south polar areas were 19,337 pounds of sauerkraut and 400 pounds of mustard as substitutes for fresh vegetables and fruit, the lack of which caused scurvy. The *Resolution* and *Adventure* left England in July 1772. It was to be three years before the crews of these ships again saw their homeland.

Despite the foresight of Captain Cook, the ships and crews

were scarcely prepared for their voyage to the frigid climate to which they sailed. Both ships, though ultramodern by mid-eighteenth-century standards, were small, dank, crowded vessels. The crews were inadequately clothed. Most of the men went barefoot, long since having worn through the patent leather shoes and roughly woven wool socks issued by the Royal Navy. Their clothes were thin and, as the months of the voyage rolled on, they became little more than outfits of tattered patches. In their quarters, the men fought one another for bits and pieces of old sailcloth, which they could add to the layers upon layers of rags they already wore, to try and keep warm in the freezing antarctic seas.

The crew were rarely, if ever, dry; their clothes soaked through by rain, sleet, snow and seawater. As they worked the ice-coated sails, high above the ship's main deck, the men scurried about on sharp ice-covered ropes and lines that cut their hands, legs and feet. Below decks, the quarters were cramped and unheated. The only fires aboard the highly flammable wooden ships were in the galley, where the food was prepared, or in the small lamps used to light the quarters. Thus the men, their captain and their officers shivered and shook through the long voyage through the latitudes of the "Furious Fifties," and the "Screaming Sixties."

On January 17, 1773, Captain Cook became the first man to cross the Antarctic Circle and enter the south polar zone. Over the next eighteen months, the tiny expedition managed to circumnavigate the pack ice surrounding the Antarctic. The knowledge collected on this voyage is impressive, even by modern standards. Captain Cook's *Journals*, published in 1777, are still considered among the most important and valuable documents in south polar exploration and literature.

Cook's tales of horrendous hardships, stormy seas and ferocious cold quickly dissuaded other adventurers and sea captains from probing for the "Great Object" which lay just beyond the Antarctic Circle. Until 1819, in fact, there is no known record of anyone's setting out to dare the icy elements in search of the snow-covered land of ancient legend.

But the great commercial rivalry between the United States and England for whale oil and sealskins spurred whalers and seal hunters farther and farther south, into the still unknown and unexplored antarctic seas. The question of who first reached the antarctic continent will probably never be known. The British, Americans and Russians all claim the honor.

For the record, the Americans claim that a twenty-one-year-old Yankee skipper named Nathaniel Brown Palmer, sailing an eighty-foot-long, sixteen-foot-wide sloop, the *Hero*, was the first to land on the continent in January 1820. Since then, American map makers have called the area the Palmer Peninsula. Located opposite the tip of South America, the peninsula is the longest in the world—twice the length of Italy.

British historians and map makers, however, have hotly challenged the American claim and the name of the peninsula. They call it Graham Land, named by Royal Navy Lieutenant Edward Bransfield who, also in January 1820, sighted the same peninsula while cruising in the antarctic waters, and named it in honor of his First Lord of the Admiralty, Sir James R. G. Graham. After generations of bitter controversy, the United States and Great Britain in 1964 agreed to compromise on the name of the peninsula, and now the two nations call it the Antarctic Peninsula.

It was on Palmer's return from his first trip to the Antarctic Peninsula that the first of the now never-ending "It can only happen in the Antarctic" stories occurred.

En route to its sealing base, Palmer's vessel was suddenly enveloped by a thick fog. Afraid of drifting into an iceberg, the young captain hove to, dropped anchor and cancelled all watches. Several hours later, the fog slowly lifted, and Palmer found his tiny sloop neatly parked between two towering, powerful men-of-war.

Palmer immediately broke out the Stars and Stripes. As the

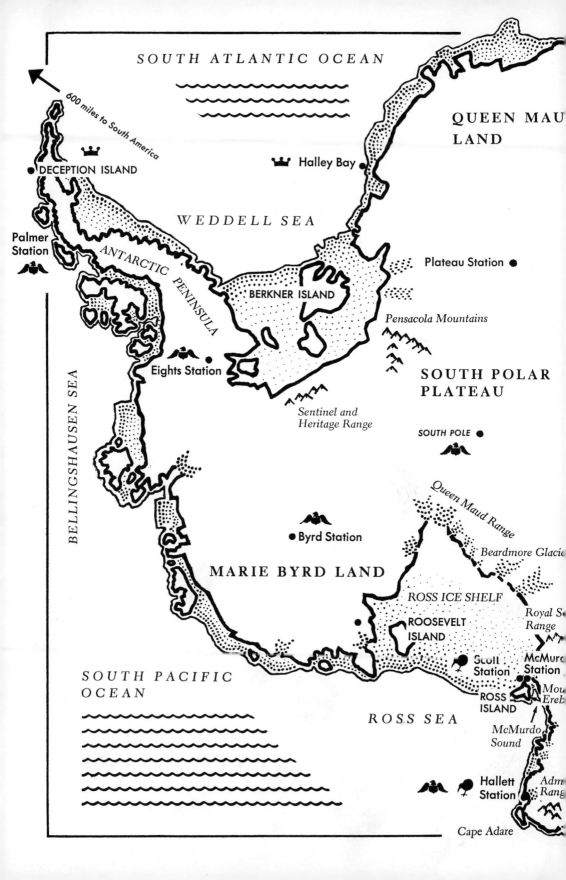

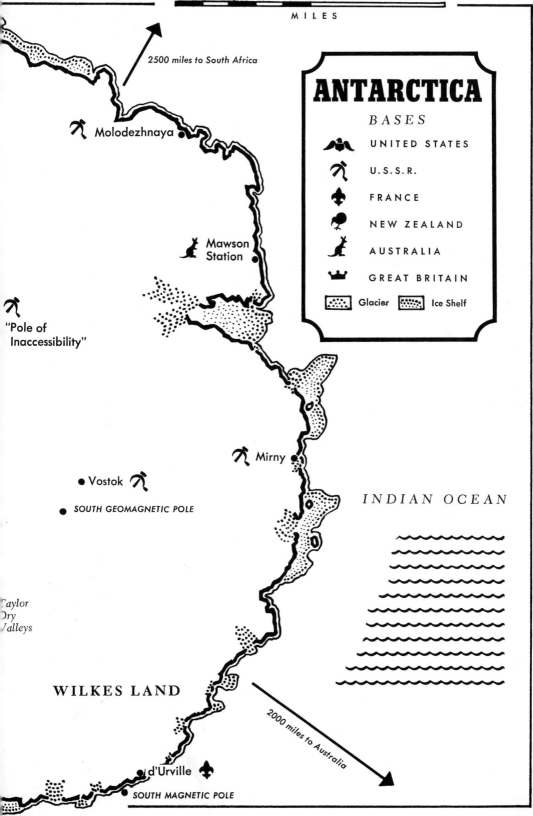

flag slowly fluttered up the staff and caught the wind, the two warships hoisted their standards in reply. The flags were of Imperial Russia. In all those vast seas, Palmer had come to anchor in the very middle of the first Russian Antarctic Exploration Expedition, led by Admiral Fabian Gottlieb von Bellingshausen. It is worth noting that the Russians, too, claimed the first sighting of the antarctic continent in January 1820.

Between 1838 and 1840, Great Britain, France and the United States each officially mounted a major south polar expedition. The chief goal of the British expedition was to reach the South Magnetic Pole. The venture was led by Royal Navy Captain James Clark Ross, famed and respected for having spent fourteen years in the Arctic hunting for, and eventually discovering, the North Magnetic Pole. He was obsessed with the idea of planting the very same flag used at the North Magnetic Pole at the South Magnetic Pole too.

The American expedition, led by Navy Lieutenant Charles Wilkes, was charged with charting the South Pacific and antarctic waters. Made up of six leaking hulks, probably no polar expedition, before or since, left port more ill-prepared or disorganized.

The French expedition was under the command of Captain Jules Dumont d'Urville who, in the course of his career, had sailed every known sea of the world. He was also the discoverer of the famous statue, Venus de Milo. D'Urville's ambition was to give France the glory of sailing closer to the South Pole than had any other nation.

On January 19, 1840, d'Urville sighted the towering white cliffs of the antarctic coastline. However, he was determined to see the land which lay beyond those majestic, desolate cliffs. After much difficulty, he eventually succeeded in getting a small boat ashore in a sheltered cove among the steep overhanging rocks. There the boat crew, led by d'Urville, planted the tricolor of France in the snows, broke open bottles of wine, and drank the health of their king.

Lo and behold, up from the sea, one after another, popped "a kind of bird, black all over with a yellowish-white chest and blinking yellow eyes." The bird, "which walked like a man," blinked at the strangers. D'Urville and his men, none the worse for the wine, blinked unbelievingly back. Then the birds, "boldly strode up to us and began following us about." D'Urville was so taken with the strange birds, he named them after his wife, Adélie, and to this day this species of penguin is known as the Adélie. One question is invariably raised among men who have seen these delightful, strange birds waddling about in their native habitat: If the Captain named these penguins for his wife, what could Madame d'Urville possibly have looked like?

In addition to naming the penguins, d'Urville also named the rugged coastline on which he landed Adélie Land and, unwittingly, put himself in conflict with Wilkes, who, on the same day, January 19, 1840, in the same area, a hundred miles away, also took possession of the land, naming it Wilkes Land in honor of himself. The United States and France disputed the claim for 110 years. Then, on January 19, 1950, a French antarctic expedition landed along the Adélie Coast, set up a base camp called d'Urville, and have manned it ever since, settling the matter, in their minds, at least, once and for all.

A few days after the simultaneous landfalls, d'Urville, sailing west, and Wilkes, sailing east, encountered one another. And another "it can only happen in the Antarctic" incident took place. As the ships approached, neither knowing who the other was or what it was doing in the forbidding waters, d'Urville ordered the French tricolor run up to identify his vessels. For reasons never revealed in the log of Wilkes's ships, the Americans refused to raise their colors, or to fire a courtesy salute to the French. The French, snubbed, ordered more sails set as a return insult to the American breach of naval courtesy. The Americans, in turn, piled on all the canvas their masts could carry and, without so much as a brief "ahoy," the ships of the first French Polar Expedition and those of the first American Antarctic Expedition haughtily passed one another in the most lonely, forbidding sea in the world.

A year after the d'Urville–Wilkes encounter, Captain Ross crunched through the pack ice which barred approaches to the antarctic continent and discovered the open waters of what is now called the Ross Sea. Sailing farther south, he sighted a great mountain peak which spewed clouds of steam. In the evening, for winter was approching and the sky darkening, a reddish tint painted the plume of steam. Gazing in wonder, Ross and his crew suddenly realized they had come upon an active volcano, which they proceeded to name Mount Erebus in honor of the expedition's flagship. Ross then sailed even farther south until he was blocked by a massive wall of ice, twice as tall as the masts of his ship. The ice wall proved to be Ross's most important discovery in the Antarctic and bears his name, the Ross Ice Shelf.

This ice shelf is a frozen sea, the size of France, and in places two thousand feet thick. The vast ice sheet moves north from the antarctic mainland at the rate of four feet a day and is the source of most of the icebergs of the South Pacific. Some of these bergs have been measured to be the size of the state of Connecticut. Unfortunately, Ross never found the South Magnetic Pole nor realized his dream of being the first man to discover both navigational compass points.

From the time of Ross's voyage until 1895, interest in antarctic exploration flagged. Then, in that year, the Sixth International Geographical Congress met in London and declared, "The exploration of the Antarctic is the greatest piece of geographical exploration still to be undertaken." Britain, France, Belgium, Germany and many other nations, all in the throes of expansionism, colonialism and nationalist fervor, once again turned their eyes south to the bottom of the world.

Adventurers, driven by dreams of glory for themselves and their fatherlands, vied to become the first man to plant his country's flag at the South Pole. The hysteria culminated in 1911–1912, in a race to the Pole between the Norwegians, led by Roald Amundsen, and the English, led by Captain Robert Falcon Scott. Both Amundsen and Scott were famed polar explorers; Amundsen for his treks in the Arctic, and Scott for his previous expedition to the Antarctic. Both were great leaders and great men.

It was during Scott's first expedition to the Antarctic, in 1901–1903, that aerial observation and photography were introduced to the white desert. Using a captive balloon tethered to the deck of his ship, the *Discovery*, Scott rose 790 feet. Floating high above the snows, he could see hundreds of miles in all directions. The wind, however, set the balloon into a dizzy swinging motion, which proved too much even for an old sea dog like Scott.

Others who attempted to reach the Pole, besides Amundsen and Scott, included Sir Ernest Shackleton, who, in 1907, brought the first automobile to the Antarctic. He hoped to drive to the Pole. But the car proved cranky and coughed to a stop after a drive of a few hundred yards in the snows. Eventually the car was abandoned.

Shackleton, who had been on Scott's 1901–1903 expedition, set out for the Pole in 1908 with three companions and enough provisions for ninety-nine days. A month after leaving his base camp, Shackleton discovered the so-called Pathway to the Pole, the mighty Beardmore Glacier. The Beardmore, largest glacier in the world, is 160 miles long, sixty to eighty miles wide, and rises eight thousand feet from the frozen Ross Sea to the South Polar Plateau.

It took Shackleton and his companions twenty-two days to reach the top of the Beardmore. Just 110 miles from the Pole, Shackleton paused to take stock of his provisions. To his horror, he found he had enough food for only forty more days in the field. With a decisiveness which was one of his principal characteristics, Shackleton broke off the trek, planted the Union Jack

where he stood, and turned back, "having done the best we could."

Scott, hearing of Shackleton's failure, again took up the challenge of conquering the Pole for England. In 1910, as he organized his expedition, Amundsen of Norway was also making preparations. While Scott's expedition was based on attaining the Pole, it was also highly scientific in nature as well. Amund-

The Beardmore Glacier, seen from the Polar Plateau

sen's sole purpose was to reach the Pole and return as quickly as possible—fame and fortune were his goals. And Amundsen achieved them both.

With four other men and fifty-two dogs, Amundsen started off from his base at Framheim, on the Bay of Whales, on October

19, 1911. From the outset, the trip was smooth, rapid and un-
eventful. Even the weather was kind. Scott, based on Ross
Island, eighty-seven miles farther north of the Pole than
Amundsen, left his camp on November 3, 1911. With him
were Dr. Edward A. Wilson, Petty Officer Edgar Evans, Captain Lawrence E. C. Oates, and Lieutenant Henry R. Bowers.
Their journey was staged with the help of Manchurian ponies.
As the ponies fell by the wayside, Scott and his men became
their own beasts of burden, manhauling their sledges the rest
of the way. Manhauling sledges is not as difficult as first appears for sails were often mounted to masts erected on the
sledges. Taking advantage of the wind, the party was often able
to sail across the snowy plains.

While Scott and his party were still struggling toward their
goal, Amundsen's sledges, on December 14, 1911, slid to a
halt at 90° south—the South Pole. There was nothing to be seen,
in any direction, except a flat, unbroken blank expanse of snow.

In a voice cracked with emotion, Amundsen quietly announced to his four companions, "Our goal has been reached."
Then the Norwegian flag was taken from its case, and Amundsen
and his men, each grabbing hold of the flag's pole, raised it as
the first at the bottom of the world. So doing, Amundsen pro-
claimed, "Thus we plant thee, beloved flag, at the South Pole
and give to the plain on which it flies the name King Haakon VII
Plateau."

The Norwegians remained at the Pole for three days. When
they departed on December 17, they left behind a silk tent in
which they placed souvenirs of their visit, together with a letter
addressed to Scott asking him to bring back, on his return, a
letter written by Amundsen to King Haakon.

A month later, on January 16, 1912, as Amundsen was nearing his base camp, a member of Scott's party spotted a black
speck in the distance—Amundsen's tent. Scott's fears of being
beaten to the South Pole were realized. Here are his trail notes:
"Jan. 17, 1912: The Pole yes, but under different circumstances
from those expected. . . . Great God, this is an awful place and

terrible enough for us to have labored to it without the reward of priority. Well, it is something to have got here. Now for the run home and a desperate struggle. I wonder if we can make it?"

The journey of Scott and his party from the South Pole to their death is chronicled by Scott in what is undoubtedly one of the most amazing diaries ever written.

The return march of Scott and his party proceeded from one misfortune to another. Even so, Scott continued to make scientific observations and collect rock specimens and fossils, which finally confirmed to the world that life once existed on this now dead continent.

On February 17, 1912, Edgar Evans died as a result of a fall. Then the weather deteriorated; temperatures dropped into the −40°s F. and the wind snapped a steady thirty-five miles an hour. What little strength the men had was quickly sapped by the sledge hauling. Despite all the ill-luck that could be heaped on man, Scott and his remaining companions kept up their spirits. Read from Scott's *Journal* of March 5, 1912: "Regret to say things going from bad to worse. . . . We mean to see the game through with the proper spirit, but it's tough work to be pulling harder than we ever pulled in our lives for long hours and to feel the progress so slow. One can only say, 'God help us!' and plod on our weary way, cold and very miserable though outwardly cheerful."

On March 17, a blizzard struck and Oates, who had been suffering from severe frostbite and could barely move, wearily crawled from his sleeping bag, disappointed to find himself still alive. He turned to his three friends and said, "I am just going outside and may be some time." As Scott wrote, "He (Oates) went out into the blizzard and we have not seen him since . . . we knew he was walking to his death but though we tried to dissuade him, we knew it was the act of a brave man and an English gentleman. We all hope to meet the end with a similar spirit and assuredly the end is not far."

Five days later, on March 21, only eleven miles from a supply

Scott's hut at Cape Evans on Ross Island. From this site Scott left on his ill-fated expedition to the South Pole in 1911.

depot which would have saved their lives, Scott, Wilson and Bowers were pinned down by a fierce blizzard. On March 29, 1912, the last entry in Scott's trail journal was recorded: "Since the 21st we have had a continuous gale . . . every day we have been ready to start for our depot eleven miles away, but outside the door of the tent it remains a scene of whirling drift. I do not think we can hope for any better things now . . . it seems a pity but I do not think I can write more." The writing trailed off in a scrawl and was signed, "R. Scott." Beneath his name was the notation, obviously made with great effort, "For God's sake, look after our people."

Eight months later, in November 1912, Scott, Wilson and Bowers were found by the remainder of the expedition who had waited in vain through the long antarctic winter night for their leader's return. When Scott's tent was shoveled clear, he was found with his two fellow explorers, huddled together in peaceful slumber, Scott's arm thrown over the shoulder of his dear friend Wilson. Beneath Scott's body were his journals and a series of letters to friends, to the wives of his companions and to the public at large, all written within hours of his dying moments. These letters and the trail journals of Scott are classics of heroism.

His last letter—to the public—read in part, "We are weak and writing is difficult. But for my part I do not regret this journey which has shown that Englishmen can endure hardships, help one another and meet death with as great a fortitude as ever in the past. We took risks, we knew we took them; things have come out against us, and therefore we have no cause for complaint. We bow to the will of Providence, determined still to do our best to the last. But if we have been willing to give our lives to this enterprise which is for the honour of our country, I appeal to our countrymen to see that those who depend on us are properly cared for. Had we lived, I should have had a tale to tell of the hardihood and courage of my companions which would have stirred the hearts of every

Englishman. These rough notes and our dead bodies must tell the tale."

The Pole conquered, Sir Ernest Shackleton, in 1914, decided to attempt "the last great polar journey that can be made"— the overland crossing of the Antarctic from coast to coast. As Shackleton and his expedition prepared to sail for the Antarctic in August 1914, World War I broke out. The expedition was all for abandoning the venture and offering its services to the Royal Navy. The First Lord of the Admiralty replied with a one-word telegram, "Proceed." That First Lord of the Admiralty was Sir Winston Churchill.

Once in the antarctic waters, Shackleton's ship, the *Endurance*, was beset by heavy pack ice. One of the crew described the vessel as being "frozen like an almond in the middle of a chocolate bar." Locked in the ice, the ship drifted in a zigzag over eleven hundred miles in nine months. The pressure of the ice proved too much for the stout ship; it buckled and sent Shackleton and his men onto the ice. Salvaging what they could from the doomed ship, Shackleton and his twenty-seven companions lashed three whaleboats from the *Endurance* onto sledges and, along with other supplies, set up camp on an ice floe. Like a rudderless ship, they drifted on their floe with the rest of the pack ice toward open water.

The men were on the floe three and a half months when the ice broke up beneath them, forcing them to scramble into the lifeboats and abandon most of their supplies. Three days later, in April 1916, they made landfall on tiny, uninhabited Elephant Island off the tip of the Antarctic Peninsula. It was immediately decided that Shackleton and five others should take the largest boat and try to sail for South Georgia Island, the nearest civilization, eight hundred miles away, across the most turbulent and treacherous waters in the world.

After one of the most harrowing voyages ever recorded, the group reached South Georgia Island but landed on the wrong side of it. Since their lifeboat was no longer seaworthy, the six men added a major mountain-climbing exploit to their already incredible list of achievements. Despite their weakened condition, Shackleton and his five companions scaled the never-before-climbed mountains of South Georgia. It was forty years later before the mountains were again conquered, this time by a party of well-equipped, physically fit experts, and they almost didn't make it.

Reaching civilization, Shackleton chartered a ship to rescue the remaining twenty-two men of his expedition still stranded on Elephant Island. Two attempts to pluck the men off the island failed, but on August 30, 1916, after five months of almost subhuman existence, the castaways' ordeal ended and they found themselves en route home—and to a world at war.

The saga of Shackleton's last antarctic effort marked the finale of what has been called the heroic era of antarctic exploration and ushered in the present age of science on the frozen continent.

The first airplane to make its appearance in the Antarctic arrived in December 1912. There was, however, one hitch— it couldn't fly. Barnstorming around Australia to raise funds for an expedition to the Antarctic, Douglas Mawson cracked up his Vickers monoplane. A thrifty man, Mawson wasn't one to discard an airplane simply because it wouldn't fly. Mawson ordered the wings sawed off and the landing gear replaced by runners. The result was a propeller-driven sledge. During the contraption's first "flight" in the Antarctic, hauling supplies between the expedition's supply ship and the base camp, the engine failed. All efforts to get it going again were useless, and Mawson, with regret, abandoned the wingless airplane to the elements. Sixteen years later, in 1928, the airplane was again introduced to the Antarctic by Sir Hubert Wilkins who made the first exploratory flight over the Antarctic's snowy wastes.

But it is to Commander, later Rear Admiral, Richard E. Byrd that the credit must go for truly introducing the air age to the Antarctic and realizing the great potential of aviation for exploration and supply. From the moment of his triumphal first flight over the South Pole in 1929, until his death, nearly three decades and four expeditions later, Byrd's name was synonymous with Antarctica.

In May 1926, he was the first man to fly over the North Pole. A year later, with three others, he flew the Atlantic and, finally, in 1929, he became the first man to conquer both the North and South Poles.

Byrd's flight to the South Pole was filled with suspense. His plane, a Ford trimotor with a top speed of 125 miles per hour, was piloted by Bernt Balchen. Also carrying Harold June as radio operator, and Ashley McKinley, a cameraman, it took off from the snows of their elaborate base at Little America on Thanksgiving Day, 1929. The flight was completely routine until the trimotor began climbing toward the South Polar Plateau through a gap at the head of a glacier between mountains poking thirteen thousand feet into the skies.

As Balchen nudged the plane up the glacier, low clouds and fog hid the towering mountains on either side. Even at full throttle, the plane couldn't gain altitude. As it wobbled toward the pass in the mountains and the peaks pressed closer and closer, Balchen ordered all the survival gear and emergency rations jettisoned. As each bit of weight was dumped, the plane gained added lift and another few feet of altitude. Flying less than ninety miles an hour, barely airspeed, Balchen gained just enough height to clear the pass and break out over the flat South Polar Plateau, ten thousand feet above sea level.

After another hour, they reached 90° south. Flying fifteen hundred feet above the Pole, Balchen dipped the wings of the plane and Byrd threw a small American flag overboard. On a second pass the flags of Norway and Great Britain were dropped, to commemorate the achievements of Amundsen and Scott. Then, as the plane wheeled once more over what must be the worst place in the world, Harold June radioed Little

America and the world, "We have reached the vicinity of the South Pole. Flying high for a survey. Byrd."

Byrd, Balchen, June, and McKinley returned in triumph to Little America after a total flight time of fifteen hours fifty-one minutes. In less than twenty-four hours, Byrd accomplished what had taken Amundsen and Scott three months to achieve, and proved for all time that, though a fierce adversary, Antarctica's nature could be blunted and the airplane was the means of doing it.

A year after the end of World War II, in 1946, the United States sent a gigantic expedition, Operation High Jump, to the Antarctic. The operation incorporated thirteen ships—including an aircraft carrier, a submarine, and ice breakers—scores of airplanes, and forty-seven hundred men. During this expedition, sixty-four mapping flights were made and more than seventy thousand photos were taken, including a survey of about 60 per cent of the antarctic coastline. In all, between 350,000 and 700,000 square miles of new land were discovered. But no one is sure. To this day, the pictures made during the expedition have not been completely evaluated.

A year later expeditions from Great Britain, France, Chile, Argentina, Norway, Sweden, Australia, New Zealand and the United States were busy exploring and probing the mysterious continent. It remained, however, for the concept of the International Geophysical Year to incorporate these previously separate efforts and independent national expeditions into one united endeavor.

The idea of an International Geophysical Year—during which men from all over the world join forces to resolve as many of the secrets of science as possible—is not new. But the idea of having an IGY in the mid-twentieth century was startling, in view of the cold war and the differences between East and West. However, the plan took shape in 1950, and two years later a committee of scientists representing nearly every civilized nation on earth decided upon the date the coordinated

international scientific work would begin. The date was finally
set: IGY was to run from July 1, 1957, through December 31,
1958.

The Soviet Union, which, until 1955, remained aloof about
participating in studies in the Antarctic, suddenly announced
that it would join the other nations. Indeed, the scope of the
Soviet Union's commitment to the Antarctic rivaled that of
both the United States and Great Britain. In retrospect, many
diplomats feel that Russia's joining with other nations in exploring the Antarctic marked the first positive break in the cold war.

In December 1955, thirteen ships carrying expeditions from
seven nations converged on the coast of Antarctica to begin the
task of setting up bases for IGY operations. Three years later,
at the end of the IGY, twelve nations had established fifty bases
on earth's last and least known land.

The South Pole—temperature −55° F.

The United States called its "establishing" expedition Operation Deep Freeze, a name which has since stuck with each succeeding antarctic expedition sent. During the 1955-1956 season, the United States set up bases at McMurdo Sound and Little America V, and surveys were carried out toward establishing a base at the South Pole itself. A six-hundred-mile overland traverse was also completed to check on the possibilities of installing a scientific station on the desolate polar plateau of Marie Byrd Land, six hundred miles north of the South Pole. The later settlement of Byrd Station was the result.

The year before the IGY went into effect on October 31, 1956, Admiral George Dufek, leader of Operation Deep Freeze, flew to the South Pole, landed, and became the first person since

Amundsen and Scott to set foot at the Pole. Later that year South Pole Station, officially named Amundsen-Scott Base, was built. All the buildings, supplies, fuel and personnel were parachuted or brought in by air. It has been estimated that the cost of establishing the first seventeen men at South Pole Station was $1,000,000 per man. Pole Station has been manned ever since.

When the IGY concluded on the last day of 1958, the world was staggered by its success. More than sixty thousand scientists from sixty-six nations had worked in complete harmony. Over two thousand scientific stations, from drifting ice camps in the Arctic ocean to under-ice bases in the Antarctic, had been established. Observations and scientific data were collected, evaluated, and coordinated at three world centers and then made available to all the scientists and participating governments of the world.

The tally of IGY achievements in the Antarctic alone was tremendous. For eighteen months the scientists studied the sparkling snows and the unpredictable skies. Thanks to careful planning, there were few overlapping scientific programs. And for the first time, an overall description of the continent began to take form. Weather reports were tabulated and classified and examined, and a pattern in south polar weather began to become discernible.

After thousands of seismology soundings were taken, the contour of the solid ground under the snows began to take shape and the depths of the snows to be realized. But most important, all the nations worked together to discover whether the ice cap of the Antarctic was growing or shrinking. This was one of the primary IGY studies in the Antarctic, for its effect on climate and ocean levels of the world will certainly affect our lives, the lives of our children, and our children's children.

But perhaps the greatest development of the IGY work in the Antarctic was an intangible one—the realization that in the Antarctic there was room for men of goodwill.

TWO

ON January 17, 1912, Captain Robert Falcon Scott and four members of his expedition stood at the South Pole. In seven simple words written in his trail diary, Captain Scott summed up the Antarctic, "Great God, this is an awful place. . . ."

Actually, there is no really good way to describe this fearful land to anyone who has never been there. No newspaper report, no book, no movie, no set of photographs can adequately convey what this dread land is like or what it is like to live there.

The Antarctic is an icebound continent—a true land mass—located at the bottom of the earth, surrounded by the wildest seas of the world, and containing the most ferocious climate known to man. And the Antarctic is beautiful. It is bleak, haunting, magnificent, unearthly.

To visualize this land, imagine, if you can, your earliest idea of the great Sahara Desert in Africa. Conjure up barren open plains as far as the eye can see, flat and endless, with no trace of vegetation on the whole of this vast expanse—not a weed, not a twig, not a bit of brush whatsoever.

That is what the Antarctic's polar plain is like. But instead of sand, there is snow, dazzling white and of crystal-cutting consistency. Instead of sweltering heat there is a cold so intense, in

Above: *A glacier tongue, 500 feet thick, reaches into the sea.*
Right: *A lone penguin overlooks the Ross Sea.*

some places, that a deep breath burns your throat and lungs. Instead of the slow, soft desert breeze there is a fierce, slashing, unrelenting gale against which you must walk almost bent over double to keep a foothold.

Here and there on this huge continent, spectacular mountain ranges rear up through the snow and ice, their sheer stone walls soaring straight up to heights over sixteen thousand feet. In and among these mountains, glaciers—moving rivers of ice often five thousand feet thick, 156 miles long and sixty miles wide—wend their way down eight thousand feet from the South Polar Plateau to the Ross Sea Ice Shelf, a frozen body of water which only finds open sea five hundred miles from the antarctic land mass.

The Antarctic is the size of Europe and the United States combined, but to this day, only 1 per cent of it has been seen by man. Upon this continent sits a cap of ice, the volume of which has been computed to be seven million cubic miles. If all this ice were to melt at one time, it would raise the level of all the oceans of the world a full two hundred feet—high enough to flood most of the world's major cities and reach the nose of the Statue of Liberty in New York Harbor.

Antarctica is the highest, driest, coldest, windiest continent on our earth. The land averages six thousand feet above sea level, has an estimated average winter temperature of about −65° F. (A low of −129° F. was registered at the Russian base of Vostok on August 24, 1960.) The winds howl an estimated average of thirty miles an hour, and gales of over two hundred miles an hour have been clocked off the coasts. And, of course, Antarctica is dry. There is no such thing as rain, only snow, and once it falls, it never melts.

This great continent is odorless and vaporless. Nothing has ever been known to rot or rust there. Food caches left by Captain Scott in 1903 and by Sir Ernest Shackleton in 1912 were uncovered by expeditions forty years later and the food found to be perfectly preserved and edible.

To map makers and navigators, the South Pole is known as "90° south." It is where all the navigational lines of longitude converge. Look at a map and you'll see that all the imaginary lines that guide sailors and fliers around the world come together at the South Pole (and the North Pole too). Because of this, there is no such thing as "time" at the South Pole. Time is whatever you decide it to be.

At the South Pole, a man weighs exactly one pound more than he does at the equator. This is due to the flattening of the earth at its axes (the South and North Poles) and the thickening of our planet at the equator, caused by the centrifugal force of the rotation or spinning of our earth. When a person stands at the South Pole he is closer to the center of earth than if he were standing anywhere else on our planet.

There are only two seasons in the Antarctic, winter and summer, and both are six months long. The winter is six months of utter darkness and no sun, and the summer is six months of constant daylight and no darkness; in the winter the sun never rises, and in the summer the sun never sets.

How does the Antarctic compare with the Arctic? As we have said, the Antarctic is a land mass, entirely covered by snow (in some places to depths of over ten thousand feet) which completely surrounds the South Pole. The Arctic, on the other hand, is a flat, sea-level ice floe floating around the North Pole on an ocean ten thousand feet deep. Both the Arctic and Antarctic are cold, but the Antarctic is far, far colder. The seasons are similar; six months of daylight and six months of night, but they are reversed. When it is winter, or night, at the North Pole, it is summer, or daylight, at the South Pole.

Physically, too, the two polar caps are quite different. The Antarctic is a continent and the Arctic a sheet of floating ice. The Arctic, however, is surrounded by land; the continents of Europe, Asia, North America and the huge island of Greenland. The Antarctic, at the opposite end of the earth, is surrounded

The final sunset of the year at Eights Station

entirely by violent stormy seas—the South Pacific, Indian, and South Atlantic Oceans. In the north polar areas, more than a million persons live, and have lived, for centuries. Within the Arctic Circle forests abound, animals flourish, birds nest and migrate, and profitable industries, such as mining, lumbering, and even tourism, prosper. It is an area well known to man. In the Antarctic, however, all is magnificent desolation. The continent is totally lifeless except for seals, penguins, skua birds, and a handful of scientists and explorers who have "gone south."

Recently, other forms of life in the Antarctic have been found: insects which cannot fly or walk but hop around like fleas, and mites which are as light as a piece of spider web and hibernate through the six-month winter.

Vegetation is plentiful in the Arctic, but there isn't a single bit of native greenery to be found on the 5,100,000 square miles of the antarctic continent. Here and there lichen, the simplest form of plant life, can be found in *its* simplest form on rocks exposed to the summer sun.

According to geologists, the antarctic continent is about 160,-000,000 years old and was once a subtropical land, rich in luxuriant vegetation. Through millions of years and succeeding ice ages, Antarctica was transformed to its present state of refrigeration. How and why are the questions which bring scientists to the Antarctic today.

Over 90 per cent of the world's ice sits on top of the Antarctic. At the South Pole, the altitude is ninety-two hundred feet above sea level and the thickness of the ice is estimated to be eighty-three hundred feet—one and a half miles in depth. Using computers, scientists have calculated that if all the ice and snow were removed from the Antarctic, the land under the snow and ice would rise eighteen hundred feet from its present level, relieved by the loss of weight of the trillions of tons of snow now compressing the land. Some scientists further believe that were it not for the Antarctic's heavy ice cap, the earth might go lopsided and be thrown out of its orbit around the sun.

However, the story of the Antarctic is told, not by the gales and snows and forbidding temperatures, but by the struggles of man and men to set up bases and live in this blank expanse, seeking the keys that will unlock the secrets of a desolate land.

Years ago, men went to the Antarctic "because it was there." They went to conquer nature; in many cases, they were conquered by it. Today scientists and explorers from all over the world travel to the Antarctic, not to overcome nature, but to understand it. And by understanding this fearful place—its climate, geology, atmosphere, weather and snows—the scientist feels he may find some of the answers to the mysteries of nature, the history of our earth and the place of our earth in the universe.

What secrets the antarctic snows will yield to man's study and research only time—a long time—will tell. But a start has been made.

A range of nunataks somewhere in Marie Byrd Land. The mountains are approximately 6,000 feet high, but only about 1,000 feet shows above the snow.

THREE

IN MANY ways, life at an American base in the Antarctic is like living aboard a submarine frozen in the depths of an ocean of ice and snow.

For the six months of summer, all is surface activity; the bustle of men working in the shimmering glare of sunlight, exploring and preparing for winter. Then, as the sun sets and darkness cloaks the ice continent, the surface of the snows is deserted as the men submerge into the buildings and corridors of their bases to wait out the six months of winter.

Because of this strange life of living half a year underground, the men who volunteer for American antarctic expeditions—and all are volunteers—are screened and selected for qualities that would best suit them for submarine service. Every volunteer is carefully tested, physically and psychologically, for his abilities to cope with months of darkness, constant cold, cramped quarters and endless hours of close contact with very few persons.

In general, the men finally chosen are between twenty-two and forty—though "youngsters" of eighteen and scientists in their early sixties have also been selected. These men are above average in intelligence, married, have children, own their own homes, drive their own cars, smoke, drink, enjoy popular and classical music, aren't fussy about food, adore movies, read a good deal, are easygoing, friendly, curious, highly adaptable, and enjoy the company of others. In addition, they all have in common patience, courage, endurance, a sense of humor, and an insatiable desire to know simply for the sake of knowing.

For the time being, Antarctica remains very much a man's world, probably the only place on earth where there are no women and none are officially allowed. There have been women, in the past, who have visited the continent, but very few. In the late nineteenth and early twentieth centuries, wives of sealing and whaling captains occasionally accompanied their husbands on their voyages to antarctic waters. In recent times, women scientists were included in some of the Soviet summer expeditions.

Two women, Mrs. Finn Ronne, wife of the famed Naval Reserve Commander, and Mrs. Jeanne Darlington, wife of Ronne's second in command, hold the distinction of being the only women known to have spent a winter in the Antarctic. That was in 1948. It is said they didn't get along with one another. And in 1957, an American commercial airliner touched down at McMurdo for a couple of hours on a tourist and publicity flight from New Zealand to Antarctica. On board were two stylish stewardesses who created quite a stir during their brief visit at McMurdo. But these were isolated instances; Antarctica remains a man's land, except for the ever-present pinup pictures which, in antarctic argot, are referred to as "memory aids."

There are two groups of men who make up the American antarctic expeditions. The civilian scientists do the actual exploration of the continent and conduct the highly technical studies; the U.S. Navy personnel support the scientific activities. They are cooks, carpenters, pilots, tractor drivers, mechanics, electricians, radio operators, meteorologists, cartographers, and general all-around helpers.

The scientist-explorer of today is not the adventurer who went to the Antarctic merely to seek his fortune and make his name.

Rather, he is the young expert who seeks to learn and understand and pass on his findings to others so that a continuous
chain of knowledge will be forged. He uses the vast continent as
a great scientific laboratory for research in meteorology, biology,
geology, seismology, glaciology, physics, geomagnetism, cosmic-
ray study, and recording of out-of-this-world noises.

The scientists want to know how old the continent is, what it
looks like beneath the thousands of feet of snow, what the contour of the land is, its shape, soil content, and mineral value. To
do this, some use helicopters to scale unclimbable mountains,
landing at impossible sites to examine rocks to determine the age
of the mountains and their geologic history.

Other scientists traverse the open, snow-blown plateaus to map
the ever-changing drifting plains. They dig hundreds of feet
into the snow cap to mine cores of ice and to compare minute
particles of matter found in the almost infinite layers of ice,
thousands of years old, against similar matter found in other
parts of the earth. Some explorers devote their time to studying
the glacier flow of the ice cap to determine whether it is increasing or decreasing and whichever, how fast. Whatever conclusions

Top left: *Entomologists collecting tiny insects in the Royal Society
Mountain Range. The next picture shows rock specimens being
warmed to awaken dormant insects.* Bottom left: *Studying magnetic
energy at Pole Station.* Below: *Examining fish from the Ross Sea*

Above: A *buried microphone picks up the "voice" of the ice. From the tape recording of these sounds, scientists predict the calving of icebergs.* Right: A *rocket is launched 250,000 feet to study the jet stream.*

they reach will eventually have deep meaning for every living creature on earth.

Meteorologists stand in winds of seventy-five miles an hour, in temperatures of −55° F., launching weather balloons and carefully tracking them to determine the effects of antarctic winds on the weather over the rest of the world.

Through the six-month winter night, physicists work in tiny, cluttered laboratories under the snows, studying the upper atmosphere by bouncing radio waves off the ionosphere sixty to one hundred miles overhead, counting the number of cosmic rays which bombard the earth, photographing auroras, and recording radio noises that originate somewhere far out in space. Biologists plumb the depths of the surrounding seas, SCUBA diving to find new species of fish, and studying their

metabolism to determine how these fish survive such cruel cold and what lessons they can provide modern man.

For all this work there are tools. Some are as simple as a fish net, others frighteningly complex and sophisticated. There are theodolites for tracking and mapping, pyrometers for measuring solar radiation, riometers to measure radio noise, and high-and-low frequency transmitters and receivers to tune in on radio waves to find how they are affected by the earth's magnetic field. There are all-sky cameras to photograph the entire heavens every few seconds of the six-month night, photoelectric metering devices to measure the slightest changes in sky brightness caused by auroras and airglow, and seismographs to measure and determine the contour of the land under the snow.

During the summer—from October, when the sun rises high in the skies, until February, when it begins to set—all is brisk stir about the bases. In the temperatures of −20° F., thousands of men pour onto the ice, brought by plane and ship. They work three eight-hour shifts a day, restocking, resupplying and preparing the stations for the wintering-over personnel.

It must be remembered that the Antarctic is the most isolated continent on our globe. Nothing is native to it. Every item on the 5,100,000-square-mile ice cap must be imported, every need anticipated—from a size 13 mukluk to a spare Plexiglas pane for an observation dome. Incredible planning, timing and teamwork go into the execution of every task, large or small. Every request for equipment and supplies is analyzed as to need and priority and, along with the rest of the cargo of fuel, food, replacement parts and new equipment, scheduled for time of arrival, place of storage and date of use.

Probably the biggest task for the Navy support personnel is the sheer manhandling of fuel and supplies; the loading and unloading of ships and airplanes twenty-four hours a day, seven days a week, five months a year. When a plane arrives from the U.S. depot in New Zealand, ten tons of supplies must be unloaded as quickly as possible so that the airplane can take advantage of the weather and return to New Zealand in a minimum period of time. If unloading were to lag and the weather change, the plane might be grounded for days, and other shipments would be thrown off schedule.

As the plane from New Zealand is being unloaded, other planes, based at McMurdo, are reloaded with the newly arrived material and dispatched to other U.S. bases in the Antarctic in need of immediate resupply. Supplies which aren't immediately transshipped to inland stations are loaded on sledges, hauled from the airfield to the warehouses surrounding McMurdo, and again unloaded and cached away for future use.

Still, the unloading and transshipment of air cargo is only a minor part of the resupply work. During the summer, supply

Setting up a field camp in the Heritage Range

vessels arrive and depart with frequent regularity. Tons of cargo have to be transferred from ship to shore and then to warehouses. Fuel lines must be laid across miles of ice so the bulk fuel brought in by tankers can be pumped ashore to storage tanks built around McMurdo.

If mere handling of cargo were all that the support personnel were required to do, their task would be simple indeed. But airplanes have to be repaired and maintained, radio equipment tested, electronic circuits constantly checked, motorized equipment kept in repair and readiness, old equipment rebuilt, new equipment installed, and worn-out equipment dissected and usable parts salvaged for spares. Station buildings have to be repaired, rebuilt, or replaced; runways around the airfield kept clear of drifting snow, laundry washed and four meals a day prepared for each man.

Water supply is another job requiring constant attention. Next to fuel, which provides the heat to melt the snow, water is the most precious item on the continent. Night and day, at McMurdo and at all the other stations, special details of men called "Gunga Dins" (after Rudyard Kipling's Indian water boy) busy themselves digging out snow to provide the essential water for the various base needs.

At McMurdo a large tractored excavator noisily buzzes back and forth, twenty-four hours a day, hustling snow from a glacier a mile away to a snow-melter located at the station mess hall. Three tons of snow are needed to make three cubic feet of water. The cost of water (including man-hours required to gather snow plus the fuel needed to melt it) is about $1.25 per gallon at McMurdo, where most of the bulk fuel arrives in ships. At Pole Station, where the oil needed for melting the snow must be flown in, the cost of water comes to about $4.19 per gallon.

Because of the high cost of water and a chronic water shortage at all bases, laundry is limited to once a week and showers to once every ten days. Of course if a person feels like filling the snow-melt vat himself, he can launder and shower all he wants.

In 1964, water from the Ross Sea was desalinized by nuclear power to provide McMurdo with abundant drinking water and the prospect of a civilized sanitation system.

One of the other major tasks confronting all the men in the Antarctic is the vital fire watch. The high winds and bone-dry air, compounded by the lack of water and flammability of all the quarters, make fire an extreme hazard. For this reason, every building and billet is checked hourly by fire details. A public address system connecting all the buildings announces a fire the moment it is discovered and, at the stark cry of "Fire! Fire! Fire!," every man must turn out to fight the blaze.

Special fire trucks, adapted to operate in the bitter weather, have been designed for the U.S. bases and are manned around the clock. Since water, even if available, would freeze before it could reach the blaze, special chemicals resembling sawdust are sprayed on the fires, putting out the flames with almost numbing speed. At one time, antarctic fires were fought with fire, using flamethrowers, but the idea was abandoned. The flamethrower, being a fire itself, proved to be as dangerous as the blazes it was used against.

During the 1964-65 season, a fire at Pole Station destroyed the base garage and three tractored vehicles. The twenty-two men of the station fought the fire for seven hours in −60° F. temperatures. Fortunately it was summer. Had the fire occurred during the winter, it is doubtful that it could have been contained because of the high winds and low temperatures of −80° and −90° F.

To keep things running smoothly there are daily staff meetings among the officers in charge of Operation Deep Freeze. The enlisted men call these conferences "Beano Parties," for usually, following the daily big-brass get-together, orders come down, saying, "There'll be no this . . . ," or, "There'll be no that . . ."

Except for illness, the only reason work is ever cancelled around Antarctic stations is a white-out or a blizzard. The white-

Above: *An approaching storm renders the safety line almost invisible.*
Right: *A plane landing in a white-out seems to appear from nowhere.*

out, which resembles a bright, white fog, is a fascinating antarctic phenomenon. It is an atmospheric condition that causes the horizon to blend with the earth so that everything appears to be bone white, affording no sense of depth or shadow. Men describe being caught in a white-out as "walking around in a Ping-pong ball," and pilots characterize these conditions as "flying inside a milk bottle."

In a white-out, men get the strange feeling that they're ten feet tall. Quite often they lose their sense of balance and topple over. One driver, caught in a sudden white-out while chauffeuring a fifteen-foot-long, nine-foot-high traverse tractor from a supply dump to the main base, got out of the ten-ton vehicle to see if he could spot a red trail marker. He spent the next two hours wandering around in the white-out, trying to find the tractor he had just left, though he could hear the vehicle's engine panting loudly not twenty-five feet away.

Of all the terrifying experiences of antarctic weather, however, the blizzard is the most nerve-shattering. It can best be likened to a massive white dust storm in appearance, and a hurricane in intensity, with a roar like an express train thundering through a whistle stop. These storms, when they strike, rage for twenty-four, thirty-six, forty-eight and seventy-two hours, or even longer, and their winds gust across the plains at ninety miles an hour.

When a storm is forecast for McMurdo or other installations, it is watched with helpless fascination, first on the weather map, then on the horizon. In summer the storm is preceded by a windless, dull, lead-colored day, the grayness of the sky in sharp contrast to the dead-white surface of the snow.

One such storm that hit McMurdo began just that way. The weatherman had been alerted that a "stiff" storm was on its

Above: *Battening down for a blizzard at Byrd Station*
Right: *Walking in a blizzard at McMurdo*

way from an outlying weather station 539 miles to the east. The
weather station, Little Rockford, was buried under eleven feet
of snow and its wind-measuring devices, thermometer station
and radio antennas had been blown away by the raging winds.

Shortly after noon at McMurdo, forty-eight hours after the
storm had passed Little Rockford, a grayish white wall, like a
sheet suspended from the sky, appeared on the horizon, sixty

miles away. The flat, smudgy-white curtain moved forward swiftly, obscuring the mountains which surround McMurdo Sound. There was an ominous rolling appearance to the six-thousand-foot-high wall of snow. The top of the snow front was crested with a feathery spume, like an ocean wave with a white cap.

The men at McMurdo scurried about securing loose crates and other matériel. Windows in the quarters were taped around the edges to keep out the wind, even though they were already hermetically sealed into the building. Tractors and other automotive equipment were covered with tarpaulins which in turn were lashed down with ropes. The engines of the vehicles were left running. At the airfield, all the planes which had been grounded by the approaching storm were anchored down with steel cables secured to shackles embedded deep into the ice.

As the storm approached, the men gathered to watch the blizzard race at fifty-six miles per hour to engulf the station. It is rare in the Antarctic that a storm can actually be watched as it overtakes an installation or a party in the field. Usually, a blizzard strikes with little prior notice. Steadily and relentlessly, the wall of snow stormed toward McMurdo until, an hour after first being spotted, the blizzard slammed into the camp.

All was white. It was as if the station were packed into the

middle of a snowball. Snow and wind filled the air. Antennas hummed. Men caught outside walked backward, bent over nearly double. To stand up straight would have meant being bowled over to the ground. Some of the men clung to the sides of the camp buildings, but to no avail; they were blown to the ground where, in their heavy clothing, they looked like hippopotamuses wallowing around in white mud.

In the billets, fine snow sifted into the weather-tight buildings. It was as if some giant were huffing and puffing fine flour into the rooms. No one has ever been able to explain how the snow sneaks its way into the sealed buildings; it just does. Meanwhile, the wind shrieked and boomed and shook the quarters as easily as a dog worries a bone.

Inside, the base intercommunications system kept up a steady call of "Now hear this . . . Now hear this . . . The condition is One . . . The condition is One." "Condition One," in Navy antarctic parlance, means gale winds, blowing snow, no visibility, and all hands stay where they are, with no exceptions.

As the winds pounded, a steady tattoo pattered against the building walls—bits of ice picked up from the snow surface and driven by the winds. The men whiled away the hours playing cards, reading, sleeping, or arguing—usually about the weather.

Hour after hour, as the storm tore at the station, operations were at a complete halt. Despite all the comforts—space heaters, electric lights, warm food, books to read, games to play, comfortable cots to sleep in—the men at McMurdo were at one with the early antarctic explorers in their frustration with the continent. They could do nothing but wait out nature.

This blizzard was at least a storm for which McMurdo had been prepared, thanks to the growing number of weather stations developed and installed in the Antarctic. Yet weather in the Antarctic remains so unpredictable that 95 per cent of all weather observations turn out to be meaningless for forecasting conditions beyond a twelve-hour period. For this reason, it is a rule that whenever a man goes anywhere for any length of time, he must advise someone where he'll be or the vicinity in which he plans to be working. The history of the Antarctic is dotted with tales of men caught but a few yards from camp and spending hours in blinding storms, unable to make their way to safety, with their comrades ignorant of their absence.

As a blizzard passes, the skies overhead clear with suddenness. The sun pops out from the overcast and the snow sparkles in the sunshine. Visibility returns with startling clarity, the temperature rises and the wind drops to a dead calm.

The men strip off much of their heavy clothing and get busy picking up debris tossed about by the wild winds. Canvas tarps are removed from the tractors, and engines which have stopped

An ionosphere specialist bunked down with his machines

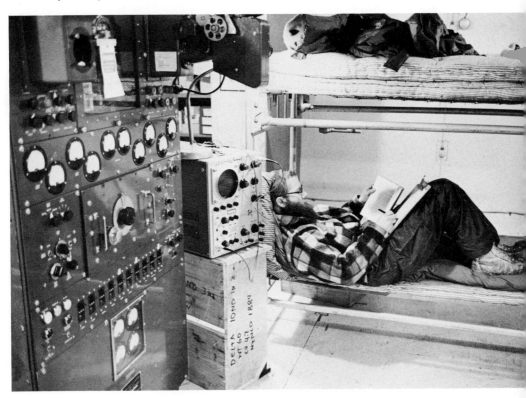

are warmed by blow torches preparatory to starting them again. In the buildings about the station, fatigue parties sweep out the snow and tidy up, and overhead the planes take up their resupply flights to the inland stations.

Working in the Antarctic is a brutal business. More than one expert has figured out that working in cold of this land of frozen time is three times more taxing on the human body than doing comparable work in more moderate climates.

To protect himself from the cold, the modern antarctic explorer may not look so hot, but he is warm. When fully attired, he will be dressed in no less than five layers of clothing plus a few extras. This will include his cotton underwear, then waffle-weave cold-weather long underwear, a wool shirt, wool trousers, a wool sweater, and a wool scarf for the neck. On top of all this is a fur-trimmed, wind-resistant parka and hood with a wool innerliner, and a pair of many-pocketed, wind-resistant trail trousers, also with a wool innerliner and drawstrings at the ankles and thighs.

On his head, in addition to the parka hood, he wears a heavy Balaklava hat which, when pulled down, becomes a face mask

with a peephole for the eyes. Last comes a special pair of sunglasses to reduce sun glare. (During the summer, no one goes
out without these glasses; it takes only a few minutes of brilliant
antarctic sunlight to make a man snow-blind.)

For his feet, he has two pair of wool socks, one thin, the other
heavy. Over these he wears clumsy, white thermal boots which
are guaranteed to keep the feet toasty-warm down to temperatures of $-100°$ F.

On his hands, he wears five sets of gloves. First skintight
cotton or sheer silk finger gloves, then a thick pair of wool
gloves over which are worn a pair of leather gloves. These three
fit into leather mittens which, in turn, are worn inside huge,
bulky trail mittens called "bear claws." And there he is, the
well-dressed antarctic explorer, togged out in thirty pounds of
clothing; a more clumsy, cumbersome outfit to get in or out of
would be hard to imagine.

In addition to all the clothing, however, there is another
touch of cold-weather protection every man on the ice sprouts
and sports at one time or another—a beard. One of the more
popular sayings of the Antarctic is, "Short men with long beards

make good napkins." The beards come in all sizes, shapes, and hues.

Naturally the debate rages in every billet on every base as to whether a beard is a good idea or a bad one. Some men swear by their beards that they are a protection against the wind and cold. Others claim just as enthusiastically that a beard is more trouble than it is worth because breath condensation, freezing in the biting cold, settles on their beards, creating icicles.

Nevertheless, every man who goes to the Antarctic and spends any time there raises face fuzz, even if it's for only a month or two. And they give as many reasons as there are types of beards. Some men think they're being practical and thrifty by saving on razor blades. Others are lazy and hate the idea of getting up those few minutes earlier each day to hack away at their face. Some feel their beards satisfy an old urge—long suppressed in more clean-shaven climes—to grow beards because they are manly and thus a man with a beard is a "he-man." One man may wear a beard because he has become bored with his face and seeks a change. Another will raise spectacularly sculptured face hair for the lack of something better to do.

But on one count, all beard-raisers agree: The best formula for a luxuriant face full of hair is just to let it grow, with a now-and-then application of olive oil. The olive oil is usually graciously provided by the chief cook who, like the others, is a member of the beard clan himself.

Because of the energy needed to withstand the cold and the biting winds, nutrition experts order a diet of between forty-five hundred and five thousand calories per man per day. This is twice the normal daily calorie requirement for more normal climates. Winter and summer, the men are given four meals a day. In addition, the kitchens are open twenty-four hours a day in case anyone wants a snack. There is probably no single item of food you can think of that isn't available sometime during a tour of duty in the Antarctic. Food stocks range from dehydrated garlic to popcorn seeds, pumpkin pie to peach flambé and everything in between, from T-bone steaks to anchovy pizzas complete with grated cheese.

Food lockers at the various American bases are stocked with a full two years' supply. At McMurdo, four huge refrigerators— yes, refrigerators in the coldest place in the world—each hold 450,000 pounds of meat and fish—1,800,000 pounds of everything from swordfish fillets to kosher corned beef. These refrigerators, each 150 feet long, thirty feet wide and eight feet high, are used to keep food at a constant temperature, not too cold in the winter when outside temperatures plummet to −70° F., nor too warm in the summer when the McMurdo mercury might zoom to 14° F. in an antarctic heat wave.

Special warehouses at McMurdo hold tons of canned goods stacked from floor to ceiling, fifty feet high. McMurdo serves as the main food depot for the continent, and all requests for food for the other stations are filled and shipped through McMurdo's warehouses. At other stations, such as Byrd, Pole, or Eights, the food boxes are stacked to form corridors, which are then roofed over and used to link various buildings under the snow.

Because good food is so important to the men's morale, the U.S. Navy takes special care to recruit the best cooks in the fleet to volunteer for antarctic duty.

Typical of these men was T. J. Miller, a Navy chef who preferred to be called a cook. A tattooed sea dog, Miller recently retired from the Navy after spending five years in the frozen wastes of the Arctic and the Antarctic pleasing the palates of the sailors and scientists on expeditions in these areas.

Most recently, Miller ran the one-man kitchen at Hallett Station, now closed. In the year he spent there with the eighteen-man wintering-over party, he served 19,710 individual meals, baked 1,189 two-and-one-half-pound loaves of bread, and served 642 mouth-watering cakes and pastries from cherry cobblers to babas *au rhum*.

The importance of a good cook at small stations like Byrd, Pole, or Eights is emphasized by the remarks one grizzled scien-

tist made after an eight-month winter with eighteen others at
Pole Station. "It wasn't so much all the other men and their
moods as it was the cook. We could always manage to avoid
one another every so often if we felt like it. But," he went on,
"we had to see the cook at least three times a day whether we
liked it or not. The mood of the cook each morning set the
mood of the station and our mood for the rest of the day. If
'Cookie' was up bright and cheerful, we all seemed bright and
cheerful that day, but if he got up on the wrong side of the
bunk some morning, we all had a grouch on the rest of the day
as well."

The favorite food of all the men in the Antarctic seems to be

Hallett Station dining room

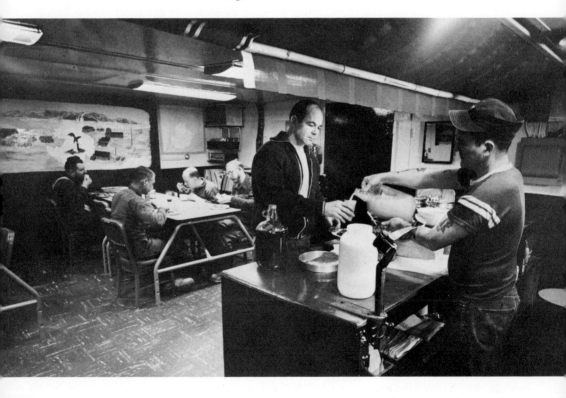

steak. Most of them dislike fish and liver. The favorite dessert is ice cream. Aside from coffee, which is drunk by the gallon, the favorite beverage is iced tea. When available, fresh milk, fruit and vegetables flown in from New Zealand arc highly prized. But the food is brought in only during the summer on a space-available basis.

Because of the bleak sameness of the landscape, all the men crave color, and the pilots and crews of the airplanes shuttling back and forth between McMurdo and New Zealand always try to bring small bouquets of flowers to brighten the surroundings. The bouquets are usually rushed to the mess halls where the men stand around and admire them.

There is little illness in Antarctica. Most medical men believe the temperature and climate are so forbidding that germs simply aren't able to survive. When replacement personnel first arrive on the ice, both they, and the old-timers who've been well through the whole winter, develop colds, coughs and sore throats. The new men, it seems, bring germs with them to the continent and spread them among the others. Until the epidemic of sniffles dies out, everyone suffers, but once these ailments pass, usually in ten days' time, there is little to fear except physical injury, an occasional stomach upset, a headache, or a bad tooth. All the stations, however, have fully equipped sick bays. McMurdo boasts a six-bed hospital with an operating room and a dentist's office.

Aside from frostbite, the only affliction every man suffers from at one time or another is "The Big Eye," a form of insomnia or sleeplessness. Its symptoms are listlessness, a glazed stare, large bags under the eyes and a grouchy disposition. No remedies other than sleeping pills have been found and, though the cause of "The Big Eye" isn't known, medical experts believe it is caused by the twenty-four hours of continual daylight in summer or the twenty-four hours of constant darkness of winter, which appear to upset the delicate sleeping mechanisms of the human body.

During the summer, while all is brightness, the land of utter silence is alive with the grinding of tractor engines, the whine of airplane turbo props, the toot of ship's whistles, the shouts of men, and the whoosh of sled runners cutting through the snow cap crust.

Then, as the sun sets, the Antarctic stations become only pinpoints of light and wisps of escaping vapor in the winter night. The darkness is broken only by the frosty light of a dead moon on a cold land, or the ghostly curtain of colored lights of aurora blazing in the heavens above.

FOUR

ON A gray, overcast, somewhat forbidding October morning, with temperatures hovering about −30° F., two hundred men, nearly the entire wintering-over party of McMurdo, stood about on the endless, dull plain of the frozen Ross Sea. Every now and then they'd stamp about in their big, white, thermal "Bunny Boots" or flap their arms to keep warm in their worn, overstuffed parkas. One man, then another, would peer north through his sunglasses toward Mount Erebus, looking for a speck in the sky from the rest of the world. They were awaiting the first relief plane of the summer.

The sun, it is true, rose in August but, as usual, hardly anyone saw the sunrise at McMurdo. Just a feeble glow of light was all that marked the event. Overcast and blowing snow hid the sun from view. Winter for the men in Antarctica doesn't end with sunrise. It isn't until the first airplanes arrive with mail and new faces and news of the outside world that the wintering-over people know that "summer is here."

On this particular day, the men had been standing around Williams Field at McMurdo since 3 A.M. Waiting. Just waiting. They knew two cargo planes had left Christchurch five hours earlier. They knew that the flight to McMurdo from New Zealand took eight hours . . . still . . . with a tailwind. . . .

One man, then another, spotted a speck in the sky. A cheer, muted by the wind, rippled through the ranks of men standing about in disorganized fashion. A few minutes later, a C-130 Hercules of the Navy VX6 Squadron, splashed with orange recognition patches, swooped down on Williams Field's sixty-five-hundred-foot skiway and slid to a halt. It was the first relief plane of the year. Winter was over for McMurdo.

Quickly the men surrounded the plane and stood about jabbering excitedly. They shouted, pounded each other on the back, took pictures of one another, pointed to the plane, danced little jigs of joy, and then lapsed back into silence to await the opening of the plane's doors.

As the hatches opened, the commanding officer of McMurdo rushed to the plane. The first man to step from the aircraft found himself all but crushed in the CO's all-embracing antarctic bear hug. "Boy, are we glad to see you!" was all that could be heard over the high scream of the plane's turbine engines and the yells of the two hundred men jumping up and down on the ice. But it was all that needed to be said.

Almost at a given signal, a hush again fell. Then the men rushed to the plane and began unloading sack after sack of mail—the accumulation of seven months. This was only the first planeload. Dozens more were to follow.

The plane also carried A-1-priority emergency spare parts and fifty-six new faces. But the mail sacks came first, unloaded quickly, bucket-brigade fashion, from the cargo plane to helicopters which stood by to haul the mail to the base post office, opened for the first time since sunset the previous March—the day the last ship departed from McMurdo Sound for New Zealand and home. At the post office, volunteer mail clerks stood ready to sort and distribute mail as quickly as possible.

For a while, McMurdo was a ghost town. Men retired to their quarters, to read hungrily the "latest" news from home, some of it eight months old. Many had been unable to make radio contact with their loved ones through the ham radio

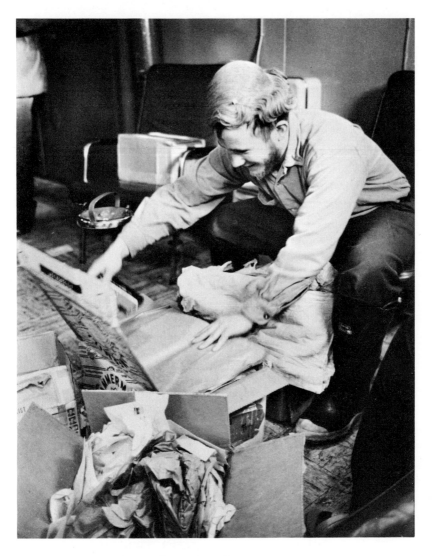

Top priority: opening packages from home

despite all efforts; these letters were the first inkling of the situation at home.

Though a joyous event, the first mail often brings heavy disappointments to many of the men. News of family troubles, broken marriages, deaths—with all the happiness of summer relief, a touch of gloom also ripples through McMurdo that first day of summer. It is a scene that is repeated in station after station in Antarctica as each installation is relieved in turn.

The winter, the six months of darkness and cold, is like a long siege—without guns and hunger, but with the ever-present roar of winds and the enforced company of the same people. Tensions grow as isolation deepens. Each man, scientist and Navy support man alike, feels an all-engulfing loss as the last icebreaker raises anchor and crashes north through the ice toward warmer waters. Winter sets in with a vengeance then, and men turn to their appointed tasks. They've steeled themselves for the seven long months ahead. At least they think they have.

But McMurdo in winter is not alone. There are also Byrd, Pole Station, Eights, and Palmer Station, established in 1965 on Anvers Island, off the west coast of the Antarctic Peninsula. Here, too, men are isolated and alone. Their vigil is longer, however, for their relief won't come for many more weeks after the relief of McMurdo. They must wait until their weather eases enough to allow flights to operate. At Palmer, the nine men must wait until the seething seas calm enough for ships to approach.

New arrivals in the Antarctic in the early part of the summer are easy to spot. They have color in their faces. The men who have spent the long night in Antarctica all have pasty, waxen complexions. They all have a faraway look in their eyes and an aimless expression on their faces, caused, the psychologists say, by the long darkness and the excessive familiarity they have with one another. Their features are all drawn.

Most of the men of the wintering-over party act somewhat listless when you first meet them. Their manner, though outwardly friendly, is withdrawn and aloof. They have a bored preoccupation brought on by too much talk about themselves and their lives with one another. It is said that after a winter in the Antarctic, every man knows his companions as well as himself, if not better.

One of the more fascinating aspects of wintering-over psychology which overtakes the men is their coolness toward new arrivals. That all the men yearn for the company of visitors there is no doubt; new faces and new conversation are almost all the men can think of during the last few weeks of winter. Yet when the new men arrive, the wintering-over group withdraws into its own cliques. The old-timers seem to fear that the security of their friendships, so painfully created during the past seven months, will be shattered in one brief encounter. And shattered it is.

After the initial shyness and withdrawal are experienced, curiosity gets the better of the wintering-over man and he soon engages the strangers in conversation that is voluble and loud. One of the easiest ways of recognizing the "OAE" (Old Antarctic Explorer, as they call themselves), aside from his complexion and reserve, is by his talkativeness once the ice is broken. They all talk too much. They seem to be unable to stay on one subject for any length of time, and jump from one topic to another, filling their ears with new voices and sounds, and their minds with new impressions. They attempt to catch up on seven months in one great big gulp. As soon as their initial shyness wears off, the old hands prove warm and comfortable companions, eager to share old jokes and pass on all the information they possibly can about life in the Antarctic and how to cope with it.

News from home, the latest in sports, the juiciest gossip and the most recent jokes are what the isolated men crave most from new arrivals. This craving led to the founding of a newspaper at McMurdo. It is called *The McMurdo Sometimer* because of the infrequency of publication. It used to call itself "the only daily newspaper on the antarctic continent," until the men at now closed Hallett Station decided that they too would have a paper and began publishing a daily sheet of news items called *The Hallett Daily Hangover*. Distance between the two stations precluded a circulation war, but the appearance of *The Hangover* forced the McMurdo editors to remove that boastful slogan from their masthead.

During the winter, however, the interest of the men in what goes on in the rest of the world is limited. Their cares are more with themselves and their problems of surviving the terrible environment. To break the monotony of the long winter, three big events are celebrated at all stations throughout the Antarctic. These annual events date back to the days of Scott's

Americans and New Zealanders at a party at Scott Base

first antarctic expedition in 1902 when the celebrations were first initiated.

The first of the annual wintering-over parties is the Sundown Celebration held about April 21, the day the sun completely sets below the horizon. The second is the Midnight Party, held on June 21, or thereabouts, to celebrate the halfway point of the antarctic darkness. There is the Sunup Party, about August 20, which marks the first appearance of the sun dawning above the horizon.

All the festivities are marked by steak fries, beer busts and costumes, and all feature an old antarctic standby, the "180 Cocktail," made of canned fruit juice and straight grain alcohol. Games are played and prizes are given for the most original costume, the longest beard, and the most amusing practical joke pulled during the evening. The parties go on for hours. Some men say they'll remember these parties to their dying day. Music is provided by records, tape recorders and impromptu ensembles.

One winter, the men of McMurdo organized what was to have become another annual winter event. They called it "The McMurdo Memorial 500," a race between vehicles and men to be held on Memorial Day. The race of five hundred yards was run by eighteen tractors—including ten-ton Nodwells, four-ton Sno-Cats, and smaller Weasels—and eighteen scientists and sailors. The course was marked out through the snow-clogged streets of McMurdo and, as the hour of the event approached, the whole base turned out to watch by the light of the aurora.

The firing of a flare marked the beginning of the race as the tractors clanked off against the heavily clothed, stumbling human competition. The race lasted nineteen minutes and was won by the men. Three of the tractors broke down from over-exertion. Because of the poor performance of the vehicles and the extra work required of the mechanics to put the tractors back into service, it is doubtful the race will ever be held again.

To relieve the tedium of the regular seven-day workweek, there are movies every night. Each base is given a large store of

Dr. Gennady Tarakanov (at left) with two American friends

films which are run, and rerun, and re-rerun. At some stations, the men get to know the films so well, they play the movies without sound and speak the roles themselves. At Pole Station, one year, the men got so bored with their store of films, they even ran them backward. At Eights Station one night, the men sat in rapt attention as a "recent" newsreel, just arrived at the base, unwound revealing *The Mile of the Century*. As the movie flickered on, James Landy and Ron Delany raced one another toward a four-minute mile, lap after lap. It was only toward the end of the mile, after three minutes and forty-five seconds of the film, that the audience realized what was wrong with the "recent" newsreel. It was over seven years old.

Besides nightly movies at all the stations, there are card games and other activities including bowling at McMurdo, which has a two-lane alley, and league competition through the winter. There are also Ping-pong and miniature shuffleboard tournaments to occupy the men in their spare time.

At McMurdo and Byrd, classes were organized in history, languages, the general sciences, mathematics, and metalwork. The teachers couldn't have been better; scientists handled the math and science courses, sheet workers the metal classes, and Annapolis graduates the language instruction. Each man who completed the courses was given a certificate describing the student as a graduate of the University of Antarctica.

In 1963, one of the highlights of the University of Antarctica was a course in Russian given at McMurdo by the Soviet exchange scientist of that year, Dr. Gennady Tarakanov, a meteorologist from Leningrad. It should be noted that both the United States and Russia, as well as many other nations exploring the Antarctic, exchange scientists, permitting them to conduct special research programs at various bases throughout the continent. The United States, for example, has sent several American scientists over the past years to work at the Soviet base at Mirny and, just as often, Russian scientists have wintered-over at McMurdo. This kind of cooperation is an outgrowth of the spirit of the International Geophysical Year.

When Dr. Tarakanov first arrived at McMurdo, his English vocabulary was limited to only one word, "please." Within a few weeks, this shy Russian, with twinkling blue eyes behind gold-rimmed glasses, had become the mascot of McMurdo. Six months of daily kidding, American movies, rock 'n' roll music, political banter, and the classes he conducted in Russian for the men, made him a real "hep cat" whose favorite expression had become "not bad."

When he first arrived, Dr. Tarakanov had been somewhat apprehensive about his reception at the American station. He was no sooner billeted at McMurdo than the men began to visit with him and they nicknamed him "Gin." As Dr. Tarakanov put it, "I thought to myself, what kind of a name is this for a scientist? 'Gin,' why that's the name of a liquor. What does it mean, the Americans calling me 'Gin'? But then everyone was so friendly and they all started calling me 'Gin,' I realized it was to be my nickname. So, all right, I'm 'Gin.' "

Dr. Tarakanov learned to dislike our Western movies: "too violent"; enjoy our whisky: "like a fine vodka, it warms the gullet"; swoon over our cheeseburgers: "they're like our cosmonauts, out of this world"; and fall in love with the Americans: "a kind, wonderful, warm, warm people."

Some of the men, bored with the movies, games, studies and other organized recreation, try to come up with off-work activities of their own. One brave soul thought ice-fishing might be a sport to interest other jaded McMurdoites. He spent nine days chopping a hole through fifteen feet of ice in the Ross Sea. Then he spent hour after hour in the light of the bright Antarctic moon waiting for a nibble on his dropline. Eventually he pulled in a few local *Trenatomus Bernacchii,* a species of fish common to antarctic waters. But no one could say positively whether the hardy angler ever ate his catch.

The most popular place (after the mess hall) at all American antarctic stations is the ham radio shack. Here the men line up, day after day, to try to make radiotelephone calls to their families and friends in the world beyond the icebound coasts of their isolated continent.

At McMurdo, whose call letters are Kc4USV, the ham shack, which is really a Quonset hut, is like an old-fashioned country store. All the men stop in on their way to and from work to hear the latest news and gossip from the radio operator before it gets around the camp or is published in the *McMurdo Sometimer.* In 1963, the pride of Kc4USV was the fact it had the final score of the last Dodger-Yankee World Series game four minutes after play ended.

Ham radio is not a plaything to the men of the Antarctic. It is vital to their morale. One ham operator put it this way, "The calls the men make are as important to the folks back home as they are for the men isolated on the ice down here. It is really impossible to convey to you what it means to the men of the Antarctic, cut off as they are from all they're accustomed to—mail, newspapers, TV, home, local gossip about

The ham radio shack at McMurdo

their neighbors—and then, in all this darkness, a radio contact is made with a loved one ten thousand miles away. And is that loved one happy to hear from the man down here!"

What do the men talk about when they finally get in touch with home? First they ask about their cars. Then they ask about the children, the state of their finances, and then the health of everyone, and in just about that order.

Once McMurdo made contact with Camp Century, America's air force base at Thule, Greenland. As the radio operator said, "We both were so surprised, the guy in Greenland and me down here, we almost fell out of our chairs. We first talked about the weather and then I mentioned I was located about 839 miles north of the South Pole and the ham at Thule said, 'Now isn't that a coincidence? We're about 839 miles south of the North Pole.'" The McMurdo ham then grinned shyly and said, "I guess I was sort of shaken by that 'cause I couldn't think of anything else to say, so I signed off."

The McMurdo amateur radio station makes regular contact with about 165 hams in the United States for phone patches, completing about fourteen contacts each day. A phone patch is a radiotelephone contact where the ham operator, after making a contact with the McMurdo station, puts that contact on a telephone connection to the person being called.

Because of the distance and atmospheric conditions, phone-patch contacts between the Antarctic and the United States are always touch and go. Often the first contact comes in loud and clear and then fades into gibberish, causing great disappointment among the men making calls. A notice in the McMurdo ham shack reads, "The following reason the phone patch has been poor and faded between McMurdo and your hometown and loved ones is because the ionosphere was interpolated by antiicepherics which was hypochorused to the quadstar resulting in regent tamarind. This unfortunately leads to absolute muezzin. We're sorry. Have courage and try us again." Needless to say, the men return to the ham shack the next day to try again.

After mail, the principal craving of all the men, as winter deepens, is for a glimpse of the sun and of something green—growing green.

At the biological laboratory at McMurdo is a rubber plant that was brought by a scientist to Antarctica in 1959 as a joke. The plant, however, has been cared for by succeeding scientists of both wintering-over and summer parties and boasts its own special "greenhouse" of lights, heater and formula feeding apparatus. At last report, the rubber plant continues hale and hearty and boasts five branches. During the winter, the men often troop into the biological lab to take a silent look at the rubber plant and then quietly go back to the cold and their work. Otherwise, the only floral decorations—flowers, plants, and Christmas trees—are plastic reproductions which may be drawn from the central McMurdo warehouse. Any man may draw synthetic plants, but they *must* be returned. Failure to do so brings a fine.

On clear nights, the men sometimes crawl out of their snow-drifted billets, weather and temperature permitting, for a brief stroll in the crisp clear air. But they never stray farther than a few hundred yards in any direction from the main camp and, even then, they stay close to guide lines strung out on trail marker poles, a precaution against a sudden storm which could trap the men before they could make it back to camp and safety.

Each expedition of Operation Deep Freeze has tried to add more information about the type of person best suited to man our antarctic outposts, as well as tips on coping with the extended sense of isolation and loneliness. The U.S. Navy and the National Science Foundation, which sponsors the scientific studies on the seventh continent, make every effort to provide something for everyone. Still, the Antarctic does strange things to all the men who go there.

For those with little interest beyond their work, a few weeks of the ice and snow and the unrelenting sameness of the camp

The famous rubber plant in McMurdo's biological laboratory

routine, make them feel trapped—trapped by the circumstances in which they're forced to live, and by the sheer vastness of the snow continent they've come to try and understand. The man who succumbs to this trapped feeling quickly becomes bitter and lazy. He feels himself a prisoner in an icebox from which he can't escape. Unless this feeling is relieved by outside interests or discipline, it can cause difficulties for the group as a whole.

Often the men who go to the Antarctic do so with great expectations of finding time for study, reading, and for undertaking that pet project they've been planning to do all their lives. Too often, these high hopes are dashed by the environment and the climate. The men end up spending their spare time in never-ending bull sessions or sleeping away their idle hours in hopes of speeding the time of their departure from the ice.

For some men, however, Antarctica does prove to be a perfect place for work and study. Many scientists busy themselves during the winter, when spare time abounds, by undertaking studies other than their own specialties. The results of these extracurricular studies are often of spectacular scientific value.

There's no doubt among psychiatrists who've examined returning volunteers from Antarctica that the men who visit the great white desert are deeply affected by the experience. No one who spends any length of time there ever returns to civilization quite the same.

Many have cursed the day they set foot on Antarctica's trackless snows. Others have regretted ever succumbing to the challenge of adventure which beckoned them to those frozen wastes. But once there, they all become one with the explorers of the past, for they have shared an experience few other men have ever had or ever will know; they have been to the seventh continent of the world, matched themselves against the elements and returned to civilization different and, perhaps, better men for it.

FIVE

AS A new arrival to the Antarctic stumbles from the wind-blown skiway of the airfield toward the shelter of the airport's snow-drifted living quarters, he encounters a series of landmarks which are part of the antarctic way of life.

A few steps from the plane, pasted to the side of a drift-free shack, he may see a larger-than-life travel poster depicting a lush Caribbean island with palm trees, flowering orchids, a broad sand beach washed by gentle waves, and a handsome bronzed couple sunning themselves. Staked out beside the poster lies a team of visiting New Zealand huskies, curled up and panting, waiting for the sledge driver.

A few yards farther, on a raised mound of snow near the control tower, is a plot of artificial grass complete with synthetic flowers and a sign reading "Help Keep Antarctica Green—Stay Off the Grass." It has been there since the airport was first gouged out of the Ross Sea Ice Shelf. After every snow storm, a man is detailed to dig out the green patch, rearrange the flowers and straighten out the sign.

But the shock is yet to come. Nearing the field's mess hall, the visitor suddenly sees a naked man, enveloped in steam, dash from a nearby hut, throw himself on the snow, roll around and, as quickly as he appeared, scamper, still steaming, back into the small hut to continue his sauna.

The trip from Williams Field to McMurdo, four miles away, is an unforgettable one. Since transportation between the main base and the airfield is always scarce, six to eight men, all in bulky cold weather clothing, crowd into the cabs of the tractored vehicles designed to carry only two. No one has ever been able to explain how so many men manage to bundle into the tractors. It is a tribute to the compressibility of the human body that the feat is accomplished at all.

The drive itself is a bouncing, bucking, jolting ride as the tractor crunches along at four or five miles an hour, careening up and down unseen hummocks of ice and snow and slithering across tracks cut in the snow previously by similarly overloaded transports and sledges.

The "road," which is really the frozen surface of the Ross Sea, is picked out by fluttering red flags atop bamboo trail markers. The markers, indicating the safest route to follow, are changed daily to allow for shifts in the pack ice caused by tides in the Ross Sea. Here and there along the route are signs put up by scientists and sailors with a humorous bent and less important things to do. One sign depicts the outline of the Antarctic, a waddling penguin, and a parachuting scientist and reads, "Welcome to Restful, Offbeat McMurdo Sound." The sign was made in California.

The first view of McMurdo from the flat, frozen Ross Sea is of a jumble of buildings set on a black bluff. This is Ross Island, located forty miles from the antarctic continent. Originally built as a temporary camp during the International Geophysical Year in 1957, McMurdo has since become headquarters for all U.S. operations carried out in the Antarctic. It is the center of all transportation, communications and supplies, as well as the clearinghouse for scientific data forwarded to the National Science Foundation in Washington, D.C. All plans for exploration and scientific studies are drawn up in

Washington at the National Science Foundation and the Offices of U.S. Naval Antarctic Operations, but the actual implementing of these plans takes place at McMurdo where the admiral in charge of operations has his field offices.

At first sight, McMurdo's ramshackle appearance reminds the visitor of an old Western frontier town. The unpaved streets, snow-covered in winter, become mud ruts in the summer when the heat from the sun is absorbed by the black volcanic rock and dust. There are no sidewalks, and all the buildings, which open onto the two main streets of the base, have a weatherbeaten, just-put-together look.

When McMurdo was first constructed, the buildings were all painted orange to make them easily visible. One year, however, the naval officer in charge of the station decided McMurdo didn't have enough of a "seagoing" look, and ordered all the buildings painted battleship-gray. This gave McMurdo an even more depressing look than it previously had, blending it in with the black dusty bluff on which it was situated.

Over the years, however, the winds and driving snows have worked away at the battleship-gray paint, and bits of orange are beginning to show through, giving the camp an orange and gray mottled appearance. One wag said he hoped the next time they painted the base it would be black; in the winter night it couldn't be seen and in the summer it would blend in with the surrounding bluffs. The installation thus would be so completely camouflaged no one would ever find it, and they could all go home.

Of all the American stations in the Antarctic, McMurdo is the only one built above the snow and on solid land. The sixty-eight buildings making up the station are of three kinds, all squat, self-contained and prefabricated. The first type, the wintering-over quarters, are rectangular, built of wood, and permanently installed. The tiny windows are sealed into the construction, which helps make the building weatherproof.

"Restful, Offbeat McMurdo Sound"

These quarters are kept warm with space heaters and blowers.

The buildings are divided into a series of separate rooms which open on a central hall. At the end of the hall is a large room with a Plexiglas picture window, again hermetically sealed into the construction. This large room is used for relaxing, playing cards, reading and listening to music. The rooms along the corridor are the sleeping quarters, and each is shared by two men, who sleep in double-deck bunks. Folding doors provide the occupants with relative privacy.

The second type of building at McMurdo, also used for living quarters, are insulated canvas Quonsetlike huts, called Jamesways, after their inventor. The Jamesways are windowless except for small transoms built into the walls over the doors at either end of the huts. Many visitors are perplexed by the built-in screens over the transoms. They are there because the Jamesways were originally designed for use in the tropics. These buildings are dark and depressing. The men sleep in double-deck bunks arranged barracks-room style, with no privacy. The huts are heated by large, oil-burning heaters. At floor level, the Jamesway is very cold—about zero. At knee level, the temperature is 32° F.; waist high, it is about 50° F.; neck level, 68° F., and above the head, the temperature soars. This is because heat rises, and cold air, since it is heavier, falls. As there are no fans to circulate the air in the Jamesway, sleeping is a trial. In the lower bunk the occupant all but freezes, while his companion in the upper bunk sweats his way through the night. The Jamesway huts are acknowledged to be far from ideal for antarctic use, but they are adequate to house summer support, cheap to install and easy to maintain, which is an important factor in financing succeeding Operation Deep Freeze projects.

The third type of building at McMurdo are the galvanized iron warehouses and repair shops, both of which have rounded roofs to prevent drifting. Except for the workshops and canned-food warehouses, these buildings are left unheated and merely provide protection for supplies against the wind and snow.

Overlooking the station, a third of the way up steep Observa-

The control board of McMurdo's nuclear plant

tion Hill, six green corrugated iron buildings mark the site of McMurdo's nuclear power plant. To many minds, the small McMurdo plant may provide the eventual key to conquering the problem of living on this ice-covered continent. Prefabricated, the plant is completely portable and designed to be fitted into eighteen boxes suitable for air delivery.

Though McMurdo's atomic power plant is comparatively new, it is beginning to cut the amount of fuel which must be imported through the heavy ice to run the generators. Year by year, the billets are slowly being converted from oil heat to heat supplied by atomic power.

The nuclear plant runs very simply. Water from the Ross Sea is pumped up, purified and distilled. The distilled water is then fed into a system of pipes running to the nuclear reactor-heat exchanger, turned into steam, which is fed to a turbine which, in turn, drives the plant's fifteen-hundred-kilowatt generator, which also turns out 650,000 British Thermal Units (BTU's) of heat per hour of steam. This steam is used to help pump more water from the Ross Sea and distill the seawater for drinking. The exhausted steam, after driving the generating turbines, is sent to special air coolers (no problem in the Antarctic) which turns the steam back into water, which is again used by the reactor.

Six months after the McMurdo nuclear plant went into operation in 1962, a fire broke out in the reactor and caused the plant to shut down. This precipitated a major crisis. McMurdo was caught with a dwindling fuel supply. Water was rationed, heat turned down, and foods requiring a great deal of cooking were removed from the menu. The resupply vessels, delayed by heavy ice, finally broke through to McMurdo with the much needed fuel just twenty-four hours before all but the emergency stock was depleted.

Plans for the construction of other nuclear plants in the Antarctic, at Byrd and Pole Stations, have been discussed for years but no action has yet been taken. The high cost of installation is one of the reasons.

In the center of McMurdo, at the head of the two main streets and situated between them, is McMurdo's famed Chapel of the Snows. It is an over-large Quonset hut with blue-tinted plastic windows cut into the sides of its galvanized iron walls and adorned with a small steeple and bell. Inside, the walls are covered with wooden plaques bearing the names of those who were members of Deep Freeze wintering-over parties. The chapel, which is used for Catholic, Protestant and Jewish services, also houses McMurdo's library of five thousand books.

McMurdo is the only station with a permanent chapel. At Byrd, chapel on Sunday is in the mess hall, while at Pole Station, the base dispensary is the makeshift church, the operating table doubling as the altar during services.

Antarctic chaplains are the busiest clergymen in the world, serving a two-Sunday week (and, weather permitting, sometimes a *three*-Sunday week). Following Sunday morning church services at McMurdo, the chaplain catches a flight for Byrd

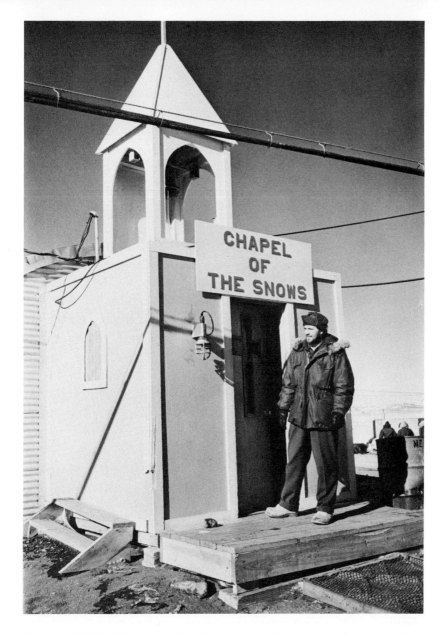

Station, 847 miles east, four hours ahead in time, but one day behind McMurdo because the International Date line runs between the two stations.

Arriving at Byrd on Saturday evening (still Sunday afternoon at McMurdo) the chaplain has supper, turns in and wakes up the next morning, Sunday, at Byrd. Here he holds his second Sunday service of the week. Then, if a plane is available and scheduled for Pole Station, he hitches a ride to the South Pole where time and day are whatever you decree. A third Sunday service is held, and the chaplain rushes off on the first available flight to McMurdo and whatever time and day it might happen to be at that station. (For scientific calculations, and for the sake of practicality, Pole Station operates on McMurdo time and date.)

Another oddity of McMurdo is the station post office which, it turns out, is Branch 17038 of the General Post Office in New York City. All mail sent from McMurdo Sound, Antarctica, to the rest of the world bears the cancellation, "New York, N.Y.," though the closet-sized branch is 12,400 miles from the main office at Thirty-third Street and Eighth Avenue in Manhattan. Unfortunately, the U.S. Post Office Department has never seen fit to give American post office facilities in the Antarctic any official recognition, much to the disappointment of stamp collectors, who often address mail to McMurdo for an antarctic cancellation. Those letters which bear cancellations marked "Byrd Station" or "South Pole Station" are really bootleg cancellations because all mail must clear through McMurdo's post office. Traditionally, however, McMurdo's postmaster simply closes his eyes when these letters pass through his office, rather than superimpose the "17038" stamp over the Pole or Byrd Station cancellation.

The Antarctic even has its own Zip Code number, which caused quite a bit of confusion when it was assigned in 1963. One day the small cubicle which serves as the station post office sprouted signs which read, "Attention all hands—your Zip Code is 96648." The wintering-over party, who had just rounded off fourteen months of antarctic isolation, were not too happy with the idea of having yet another number imposed on them. After hours of murmuring among themselves, one brave bearded type approached the postmaster and asked what this Zip Code business was all about. When the postmaster explained that the Zip Code was a new system designed to speed up the mails, the men blinked in dismay. How could you speed mails to the Antarctic when the post could only be delivered six months a year and, then, only on a space-available basis?

Aside from the billets and the warehouses scattered helter-skelter about the bluff where McMurdo is located, there are scientific laboratories for biological studies, cosmic-ray counting buildings, a rocket-launching site for firing rockets to study weather, and hundreds of radio aerials for communication with other antarctic stations and with the rest of the world. And carefully located among the buildings are thousands of crates of material and supplies. Since the equipment needs of U.S. operations in the Antarctic far exceed the warehousing and storing facilities at McMurdo, these supplies must be left out in the open. But there is little danger of rot or rust because of the cold and lack of moisture in the air.

America's second most important base in the Antarctic is Byrd Station, located 835 miles east of McMurdo and about six hundred miles north of the South Pole in the empty plateau of Marie Byrd Land, a snow-covered desert nearly the size of the United States and as flat as the state of Kansas. Here, thirty-six scientists and Navy support personnel live through the winter in five cavernous tunnels—one sixteen hundred feet long and twenty-eight feet wide—thirty feet under the ice cap. The tunnels were cut in the snow in 1961, roofed over with galvanized iron, and the blowing snow from the polar plain of Marie Byrd Land allowed to bury the site completely.

From the air, all that you can see of Byrd are three strange structures poking out above the snows: a round, windowless, khaki-colored radome, housing radar tracking equipment; a box-like orange observatory, with a clear, Plexiglas roof for aurora, airglow and weather observation; and a weather-balloon-launching platform. All three buildings are mounted on stilts about thirty feet above the snow and are connected to the tunnels below by round access shafts with ladders running up their centers. A fourth aboveground structure, a radio noise building, is located a mile and a half from the main base.

Above: *All that is visible above ground at Byrd.*
Top right: *Entrance shaft to the aurora observatory.*
Bottom right: *Main entrance tunnel at Byrd*

To enter Byrd Station is to enter another world. The main entrance to the base is a long, sloping ramp leading through blue ice toward a black, gaping hole. As you walk toward the tunnel's mouth, the snows swirl about in blinding eddies and the wind howls and screams as it tears at your clothing. Then, as you gain entry to the tunnel, there is a sudden stillness. The fearful, steady sigh of the winds ceases. Where all was glittering eye-squinting brilliance outside, all is dim, dark and dank in the great entranceway of Byrd. Bare light bulbs hanging from the ceiling dimly illuminate the way to the main tunnel.

The white snow walls of the tunnel gleam against the flickering light of the incandescent bulbs. The pant of the generators breaks the silence of the empty, spooky tunnel. All is eerie, calm and serene. Hanging from the roof above, like millions of

A typical tunnel at Byrd Station

stalactites, is hoarfrost caused by the condensation of human breath. Every so often, a soft plop can be heard as a snow-formed stalactite drops to the tunnel floor. The floors of the tunnels, like the walls, are packed snow. However, in places where there is much pedestrian traffic, duckboards have been laid to prevent the men from creating a ditch in the tunnel by their constant walking.

Lining the sides of the tunnels, adding support to the walls, are tall rows of wooden boxes—Byrd's stock of food and supplies. Three of the five tunnels at Byrd are used to store the station's fuel. In the two other tunnels are fifteen prefabricated windowless huts, each with double refrigerator doors to keep in the heat. They stand on stilts to allow ample circulation of cool air through the tunnels and preserve a constant temperature of between −4° F. and +7° F., thus preventing the walls of the tunnels from melting or buckling under the weight of snow accumulating on top of the base.

These buildings make up the sleeping quarters, mess hall, recreation center, post office and dispensary, power station, communications center, workshops, garage, and scientific laboratories.

Winter and summer, Byrd in many ways resembles a deserted subway tube. The tunnels are drafty and dark. Except for an occasional phantomlike creature slipping around the corner of one tunnel into another, people are rarely seen. Every once in a while, one of the more sports-minded of the Byrd personnel will organize a touch football game, and the tunnels will echo with the shouts and puffing of men at play. Otherwise, except for a solitary health buff taking a purposeful stroll up and down the high, narrow snow corridors, the tunnels are empty of life.

Byrd is located at 5,000 feet above sea level on 8,680 feet of compressed snow. Its winter temperatures often dip to the −80°s F. and the wind from the bare polar plains rocket across the station at seventy miles per hour, sweeping snow before it like sand from a blaster—reason enough that the men rarely venture out of the tunnels. The scientists and support personnel go "topside" only for equipment maintenance, special weather observations, or to bulldoze snow for the snow melter. The snow melter at Byrd is a gigantic tublike affair located at the end of one of the less frequented tunnels. Over the steaming pool is a sign: "No swimming in the Snow Melter. [signed] Yeti, 'The Abominable Snowman.'"

Work through the winter is steady and routine. Unfortunately, there is nowhere to go, no one to visit and no place to relax—except in the tunnels. At one time, a cupboard was converted into a peanut-size gymnasium, complete with weights to lift and a punching bag for the men to let off steam. The gym, however, was located next door to a scientific laboratory. The steady throb of the men working out at the punching bag finally got on the nerves of one particularly sensitive scientist. One evening, when everyone had adjourned to a movie, he got to the punching bag himself—with an ice pick. And that was the end of the gym.

Because of the lack of sun and wind in the tunnels from which they rarely stray, the men of Byrd are pale and lethargic compared to those of other stations. Some of the station personnel have been known to spend months, even in the summer,

Byrd Station bull session

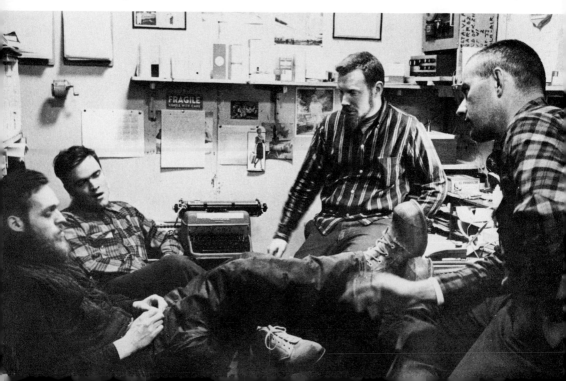

Mr. Robert Dingle with his snow traps

without venturing out of the tunnels for a glimpse of sun or a breath of fresh air. For the men in the tunnels of Byrd, time stands still. Only the dimmed, colored lights over the bunks in the sleeping quarters are any indication that there is such a thing as a night in their tunnel lives. One of the greetings often heard, in seriousness, at Byrd is, "Good morning, or is it evening? Well, 'Good' whatever it is."

Every day is like every other. The sameness is broken only by Friday's being fish day, followed by the Saturday Night steak party and the Sunday movie matinee, which runs into a Sunday night Late Late Late Show featuring "Rawhide," "The Untouchables," "Bonanza," "Ben Casey" and, most recently, "Bewitched" and "The Munsters."

The winter is entirely devoted to scientific research, with a wintering-over party of about thirty-nine men, but summer finds Byrd as busy as a village main street at Christmas time. Navy support personnel arrive by the hundreds to build, repair and put the base in shape for the coming winter. Growling tractors haul supplies from the airstrip, half a mile away, to the camp as quickly as they are brought in from McMurdo by the turboprop cargo planes. Overhead, other planes scream past in transit between McMurdo and Eights Station. They use Byrd as a navigational checkpoint and occasional refueling stop. The tunnel walls are scraped to fresh white brightness. New tunnels are hacked out of the ice and food stocks and supplies are re-stacked and relocated along the under-snow corridors. New quarters are added, others repaired. Byrd is a growing station, both in size and importance.

Scientists, by the score, settle down at the station for a summer of studies and research. Byrd is also America's principal scientific staging area in the Antarctic at this time.

One of the more fascinating studies carried out at Byrd during the past few years has been the collecting of what there is plenty of—snow. This research may seem somewhat pointless, but to one scientist at Byrd, every snowflake caught was another dot of data for his computer. The purpose of this study is to determine whether the Antarctic's seven-million-cubic-mile ice cap is increasing or decreasing in size.

A series of rocket-shaped snow traps with fins were set up so that the rockets would face into the wind to collect driven snow. The collectors were then mounted on antennas at various heights. As the snow was collected, flakes were examined under a microscope to see whether it was wind-blown (snow from the polar plain picked up by the wind and blown to another place) or freshly fallen. In one series of tests, it was learned that in one year, thirty-nine million tons of snow were horizontally driven across a one-mile front of test sites.

Mr. Robert Dingle, of the University of Melbourne, Australia, has been working for years conducting these studies. He thinks the Antarctic is shrinking. A slight man with a wisp of a moustache, Mr. Dingle says, "It is a remote, very remote possibility indeed, that in many millions of years, the Antarctic may once again be a temperate place. But what will happen to the rest of the world and its oceans should that happen, would be hard to imagine."

SIX

THERE is something terribly unreal about arriving at the South Pole.

It is cold, terribly cold; so cold, in fact, that each plane that arrives or takes off creates its own fog. The heat of its engines condenses the frigid air. Overhead, the gold ball which is the sun, radiantly ablaze in the heavens, is so brilliant that the Pole during the summer is the brightest place on earth. The snow is so white you must squint even behind the thick, dark, glare-proof sunglasses you wear to prevent snowblindness. Everywhere is nowhere, so flat is the expanse surrounding you. And only after you focus on a few posts sticking out of the snow do you realize that the bottom of the world is only a mathematical calculation. Near the airstrip, someone once put up a barber pole. Over succeeding expeditions, a store dummy—complete with blonde wig and flaming red dress—and a sign were added. The sign reads: "South Pole International Airport, Courtesy Tours by the U.S. Navy." Except for a few mounds of snow marking storage dumps, a series of antennas and wisps of vapor escaping from ventilation shafts, the only above-snow structures at Pole Station are the aurora and airglow observatory, where an all-sky camera snaps pictures of what has been described as the "most

Pole Station

splendid unearthly displays of light" to be seen on our planet, and a radome; that is all there is to be seen at 90° south.

Like Byrd Station, America's base at the South Pole, formally known as Amundsen-Scott Base, is entered by a sloping ramp leading to a hole in the ice cap. But in contrast to Byrd's gleaming thirty-foot-high tunnels, Pole Station's tunnels, barely seven feet high, are a submerged jumble of crisscrossing passageways. The ceilings are held up by a series of buckling oil drums, and crates of food supplies support sagging roof timbers. Every year, these timbers are strengthened to withstand yet another winter of increased snow accumulation overhead.

Like Byrd, Pole Station is made up of windowless shacks placed in the middle of the under-snow passageways. The eleven buildings of the base consist of living quarters, a large kitchen and mess hall, scientific laboratories, a station recreation hall, which also houses the most southerly night club and post office in the world, a combined sick-bay and radio-communications center, workshops, and a garage. Even in winter, after the summer repair and construction crews and scientists depart, the station is crowded and cramped, for the buildings are tiny, little more than over-large packing crates. Between nineteen and twenty-two men usually winter-over at Pole Station.

Going down ninety feet beneath the station proper is a snow mine which was used by glaciologists to learn the age of the ice at the South Pole and study the movements of the ice cap. The studies and tests have long since been completed and the mine is now used by the men of the station as a source of snow for the melters.

At the South Pole, though the mercury has been known to dip to —113° F., the enemy is not the cold but the slicing,

The dining room at Pole

unrelenting wind which drives the cold through many layers of clothing. Pole Station is a breathless, heart-thumping, freezing experience—breathless and heart-thumping because of the altitude of ninety-two hundred feet above sea level where any exertion is a major chore, and freezing because the mercury rarely rises above —30° F., in fact, averaging —55° F. annually. In recent years, the men at Pole have provided visitors with portable oxygen respirators to ease their breathing.

While Byrd Station resembles life aboard a submerged submarine, living at Pole Station is something out of pure science

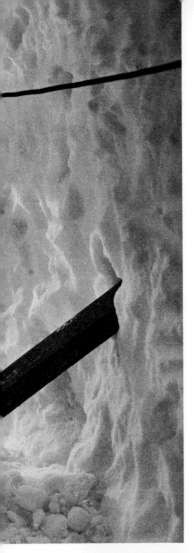

Pole's snow mine, 90 feet below the surface. Gauges in the crossbars measure movement of the ice. Below: *The South Pole horticulturists proudly show off their "garden."*

fiction. Because the base is small, you are never out of earshot of hundreds of clicking machines in the scientific laboratories. Here and there a waist-high tunnel, a couple of hundred feet long, leads to a seismograph, used to detect and record earthquakes the world over, or to instruments which study the fluctuations of the earth's magnetic field. In one building made up of layers of lead ingots, a cosmic-ray counter ticks off each speck of solar energy as it strikes the counter. And down another shaft leading to yet another under-snow shack, the steady zoom of the very low-frequency radio noise receiver adds to the cacophony of unearthly noises that blend with the ever-present whine of the wind through the antennas overhead.

One of the most exciting experiments ever carried out at Pole was achieved by two whimsical young scientists, Michael Phelan, of St. Louis, Missouri, and William Aitken, of Worcester, Massachusetts. While rummaging around the station, they found a pack of mixed seeds and vermiculite, a synthetic soil. (To this day, no one knows who had brought it to the Pole, or why.) The two scientists cleared away a section of their already crowded seismology workshop and aurora and airglow laboratory, and built a wooden trough about three feet long and eighteen inches deep. After laying down the vermiculite, they planted the seeds, and in a few weeks the seeds began to sprout—twenty feet under the polar ice cap, a mere eight hundred yards from the geographic South Pole, with the outside temperatures hovering around −90° F. From that moment on, the growing of flowers and plants became the passion of the two young men. Large tungsten bulbs were installed over the plot of vermiculite to give heat and light. The glow of a fluorescent light was added for brightness. Slowly the seeds took hold and grew.

Before the winter was over, Phelan and Aitken raised orange and yellow dwarf marigolds, carrots, calendula, and a kind of ivy. They also grew parsley but, as Phelan put it, "It looked so good, we harvested it one cold evening, chopped it up and garnished our soup with it." They also grew some onions, but they didn't have a chance. The men at the station would pass by, look longingly at the sprouts, and then crush them between their fingers to smell fresh onion and in some way realize a touch of home. But the garden flourished and the two amateur horticulturists, who had never grown a thing before in their lives, made seeds sprout, grow and flower in the Antarctic for the first time in 100,000,000 years.

A sense of pride wells up in all who go to Pole Station, those who live and work there, and those who pass through for only a few hours' visit. They are proud that this station was built at all; it was flown in—every nut, bolt, and girder, as well as food and fuel stocks and scientific apparatus. And they are proud that men can live here—in the most savage of climates, at the most remote place on earth—and successfully survive and serve science and mankind. Some, seeing beyond the present, feel that if man can achieve this, here on earth, then surely he is halfway to a similar installation on the moon.

The South Pole proper is but a short walk from Pole Station and is marked by two flagpoles set on the flat, empty south polar plain. The surface of the snow, while appearing smooth, is uneven and is called sarstrugi, from the wavelike effect caused by the wind which blows across the surface of the snow, cutting ridges in it so that the plain resembles a rippling lake of water.

Two flagpoles mark the South Pole. The taller of the two, which marks the pole itself, flies an American flag. This doesn't mean that the United States claims the South Pole as American territory, but rather that the United States is based at this point on earth. The smaller one is used as a ceremonial flagstaff on which visitors may raise and lower souvenir standards.

Because of the difficulty in reaching the Pole—only Scott, Amundsen, Sir Vivian Fuchs, and Sir Edmund Hillary ever achieved it by overland routes—less than one thousand persons have ever seen it, let alone set foot on it. Of course, when you speak of "The Pole" in the Antarctic, you must be specific, as there are five different "poles" on the seventh continent.

One is the geographic South Pole, where all the world's longitudes converge, where there is no such thing as time, where there is only one direction—north—and where it is possible to walk around the world in one second flat merely by spinning around on the heel of your thermal boot.

A second "pole" is the geomagnetic South Pole, where the earth's magnetic fields of force converge. It is 790 miles north of geographic South Pole and located at a point directly opposite a similar point in the northern hemisphere. The third is the South Magnetic Pole, where needles on magnetic compasses point straight down. This pole is constantly moving (no one has yet found out why) and is frequently located between one thousand and fifteen hundred miles from the geographic South Pole. Since its discovery in 1909 by Sir T. W. David of the Shackleton expedition, it has moved approximately five hundred miles northwest, and is still moving in a northwesterly direction about eight miles a year.

The fourth pole is the Pole of Inaccessibility, which is the point on the antarctic continent farthest inland from all coastal points. It is considered the most difficult place on the whole continent to reach. The Russians have a scientific station located there.

Finally, there is the spin pole, an imaginary point where the axis of the earth would stick out. This spot is almost, but not quite, identical with the geographical South Pole, but, being slightly out of line, traces its own small path resulting from the wobble of the earth as it turns on its axis following in orbit around the sun.

As at all the other American stations in the Antarctic, Pole Station has the usual round of winter parties, but the highlight of the year at Pole is the closely followed Annual South Pole Bowl Game. Played on Thanksgiving Day at the South Pole between the U.S. Navy and the scientists based at the Pole, the game is broadcast to all the other American stations in the Antarctic.

On the flat expanse of shimmering snow so characteristic of the south polar plain, the boundaries of the field are marked off by bamboo trail poles with red flags fluttering from their tops. The temperature hovers around $-38°$ F. and the wind blows at about thirty-five miles an hour. The altitude is ninety-two hundred feet where, if you ran fifty feet under normal conditions, you'd end up a panting wreck. Now, to the above ingredients, add thirty pounds of winter clothing per man, put the two teams in the field and watch them play. The action is all slow motion.

The Pole Bowl Game is scheduled for forty-five minutes but, because of the cold and the altitude, the contest rarely goes beyond twenty-five minutes before the men are too tired to do anything but crawl toward the goals on hands and knees. The game, in fact, usually ends up as more of a wrestling match than a football game as the men grapple with one another for possession of the ball. By mutual agreement, the umpire calls a halt when this stage is reached, and the men gratefully retire to the warm depth of the station below. So far in this antarctic classic, the Navy has won all the games.

Among stamp collectors, letters bearing a cancellation from Pole Station are among the most sought-after covers in the world. By tradition, the honor of being the Pole Station postmaster falls to the station meteorologist. And since all the letters mailed from Pole must be hand cancelled, the postmasters will tell you this is a dubious honor indeed.

The Pole post office is probably the smallest in the United States postal service. Located next to the station's recreation room and bar, called the "90° South Club," it measures barely three feet by five feet, has no windows, and is lit by one bare seventy-five-watt bulb. For eight months of the year, when there is neither incoming nor outgoing mail, the post office is closed but is left unlocked in case someone in the station wants to use it for reading. For the four months of summer, however, the small office is flooded with bags of self-addressed letters forwarded by stamp collectors seeking a South Pole cancellation.

Only once in the history of the Pole Station Post Office has there been a snag in the "mail must go through" tradition. During the 1964 Presidential election, the men of the base were prevented from casting their absentee ballots. A plane from McMurdo parachuted the ballots to the twenty-two men of the wintering-over party two weeks before election day, but extremely low temperatures at Pole Station made it impossible for a second plane to land to pick up the completed ballots.

In an isolated outpost like Pole, there are moments of mental strain, but they are few and far between. Most of the time, morale is extremely high, the men are friendly, and a feeling of comradeship and well-being is always evident about the base.

If Pole and Byrd Stations capture the imagination of the visitor, certainly Eights Station, America's newest, smallest and most remote scientific installation in the Antarctic, will capture his affection. In concept and construction, Eights Station is absolutely unique. It looks more like an automobile trailer camp than a major scientific station. As a matter of fact, Eights Station *is* a trailer camp, consisting of eight weatherproof, prefabricated, air-transportable units mounted on runners. Each unit, measuring eight feet by eight feet by twenty-seven feet, is constructed to fit snugly into the fuselage of the Navy's C-130 Hercules cargo plane. In 1962, forty-five flights of these planes ferried the units which now make up Eights Station from McMurdo, 1,578 miles away.

Once delivered, the eight trailer units were lined in two rows of four units each. Between the rows, which were eight feet apart, a floor and ceiling were laid and, using the sides of the trailers as walls, a 127-foot hallway was created, with refrigerator doors placed at either end. And there was Eights Station, completely erected and ready to be lived in, less than twenty days after the last of the buildings, provisions, equipment and personnel were flown in. A similar outpost, Plateau Station, with a complement of eight men, will be established in 1966. Located on the South Polar Plateau 1,500 miles—and almost directly

Eights Station

across the Pole—from McMurdo, the station will be prepackaged and air-transported as was Eights.

Completely portable, the camp was designed to "float" on the ice cap. When drifted over by snow, it can be dug out, disassembled, dragged unit by unit to a new site, and reconstructed. This makes Eights, and similar stations of the future, comparatively cheap, easy to install and maintain. Its design avoids the heavy expense of excavating, burrowing, and maintaining elaborate under-the-ice tunnel stations like Byrd and Pole.

Eights was designed to serve as an upper atmosphere research station, one of the first to be established in the Antarctic devoted solely to this study. It was named for James Eights, of Albany, New York, who, in 1830, was the first American scientist ever to visit and work in the Antarctic. By one of those quirks of the Antarctic, Eights Station is just loaded with "eights"—the station is made up of eight units, the measurements are mostly in eights, and the number of men originally expected to man the camp was to have been eight. However, the number of the wintering-over party was reconsidered, and the station complement was raised to eleven men—five scientists and six Navy support personnel to cook, maintain equipment, and handle the base radio communications.

Located at the base of the Antarctic Peninsula in the Ellsworth Highland between the Weddell and Bellingshausen Seas, Eights is considered the most remote of the U.S. stations on the continent. It was placed where it is to serve as a conjugate

"Whisking party" at Eights

point for an invisible line of magnetic force having its northern terminus eighty-five hundred miles away in the Provincial Park, Quebec, Canada. The conjugate point location provides scientists with a unique opportunity to study the effect of the earth, atmosphere and other scientific phenomena on the same magnetic line of force in the northern and southern hemispheres. Since little is known about this phenomenon, the studies carried on at Eights and at the installation in Canada are forerunners of a vast research effort in this field. The results of these studies are important to future space probes and rocket firings. In addition to the magnetic lines of force research, studies at Eights also include work in aurora and airglow, geomagnetism, very low noise reception, and ionosphere soundings.

Probably no base in the Antarctic is as comfortable as Eights. The compact and cozy trailers are painted orange and cream. Each unit has two windows hermetically sealed into the construction. The windows are now completely covered by twelve-foot drifts of snow, but then there is nothing to be seen anyway. During the summer, the constant daylight filtering through the snow casts an eerie, soft, blue-tinted light into the various rooms and offices of the trailers. Often the men dig a hole leading to the window and the quarters are flooded in blinding light twenty-four hours a day throughout the summer.

After each blizzard, and there are many at Eights, all hands go up to the roof of the camp to shovel off the snow. This must be done to prevent the station from being completely drifted over and eventually crushed under the weight of the snow. These "whisking parties," as they're called, are times of great hilarity and are one of the rare times men in the Antarctic ever engage in snowball fights. It takes the eleven-man crew three hours of steady, backbreaking work to clear the roof after each blizzard; often three to five feet of snow can accumulate in a matter of a few hours.

Short on space, Eights is long on comforts, including private quarters for the men, flush toilets, washing machines, clothes dryers, a sick bay, a ham radio station, a five-hundred-volume paperback library, and a kitchen which provides meals cooked to order.

The kitchen and dining area, which is really only one table seating six men, constitutes a trailer unit in itself. It is the most popular gathering place in the small station. The men sit around before and after meals, gossiping with the cook, playing cards, or simply watching the meals being prepared.

The long center corridor serves as the station's social and recreation area, movie theater and makeshift gym. The men take turns strolling up and down the length of the hall to exercise their limbs during the long winter or the blizzards of summer.

At the kitchen door in the corridor, the men have set up a social center, complete with easy chairs, coffee tables, shaded lamps, and a few paintings. There is a noticeable lack of pinups at Eights. As one sailor put it, "We're too new for that." Twenty space heaters were provided to keep the station warm through the winter, but the base is so well insulated by the buildings themselves and the snow which has drifted around the trailers that only two heaters need be in operation at any time.

To provide electricity and heat for the snow melter there are two generators. Only one runs at a time; the other is kept on a standby basis in case of failure. The constant throb of the generator is the only sound in the camp, except of course, the whine of the wind tearing through the antennas outside. For some reason, perhaps because the station is so small, all the men speak in a near whisper, which adds to the hush of the base.

One of the most distinguishing features of Eights is the profusion of clocks, twelve in all. No one knows why, but every office and quarters at Eights has a large clock. And every evening, at exactly 6 P.M., when a time signal is broadcast by the United States Naval Observatory in Washington, everyone dashes wildly about the station resetting the clocks to the time

Eights Station central corridor (top) and kitchen

signal whether the timepieces need correction or not. Correct time at Eights has become one of the manias of the station.

Though Eights is the youngest installation in the Antarctic, it has already contributed its share of "only in Antarctica" legends.

While digging out a previous American camp site which had been located near Eights, one of the men uncovered a green pitching horseshoe and a nickel under eight feet of snow. "We were digging for a tractor which was abandoned here by the traverse party of Operation Sky-Hi in 1961. Then, lo and behold, instead of a ten-ton bulldozer, we come across this horseshoe and a nickel, and nothing else."

The horseshoe has become the station's lucky piece. It is used as a paperweight, and is turned over to each succeeding relief when the camp changes hands. The nickel, however, was glued to the wall of the trailer hallway to remind the men what American money looks like; no currency is in use at Eights— everything is on credit.

The small station is unique in being the only U.S. installation in the Antarctic whose officer in charge is an enlisted man rather than a naval officer. The first commandant of the station was Chief Petty Officer Richard Steventon, a hero of World War II and a man of rare good humor and superb leadership. On July 19, 1963, he added another legend to the Antarctic.

Following a severe three-day blizzard, he sent antarctic operations headquarters at McMurdo the following message, "Attention McMurdo. Beg to report on July 16 this station visited by a six-legged bug, one quarter inch in length, brown in color, with large purplish eye in center of its head. The bug lived only one day and a half. Cause of death undetermined but believed most likely due to overfriendliness on part of station personnel. As you certainly must understand, any visitor to this remote station in midwinter night is most welcome guest be it bug or man."

With so few men manning Eights, every effort has been made

to provide them with an abundance of things to occupy their leisure time. In addition to movies and a fine library, there are boxes and boxes of complicated jigsaw puzzles, chess sets, Scrabble and Monopoly games, as well as model-airplane and ship-building kits.

But aside from the movies, the most popular leisure-time activity with the men at Eights is the continuing pinochle game. As the first wintering-over party at Eights prepared to leave, their hands were taken over by the relief personnel. It may very well be that the original game is still going on at this moment. In that first year at Eights, four men wore out nine decks of cards.

Cribbage is also popular among the Eights scientists who pair off against the Navy men in endless tourneys. And one winter, the radio man at Eights played a six-month chess match

with a fellow communications man at McMurdo. "We played one move a day every day and eventually he won. But you know what? I forgot to ask him his name."

Because of its location and the unpredictability of weather, Eights is the last station to be relieved when winter is over. As the men await the first relief plane bringing them their mail, fresh vegetables, fruit, eggs, and new faces, all is restless inactivity; they call it "channel fever." Work comes to a halt. The men pace about like caged animals or crowd about the radio shack listening for news that the relief plane is on its way. And as day succeeds day, the gloom deepens.

When news of a plane en route is finally shouted down the corridor the men stand about in disbelief. Then all is bustle; the "fever" is broken. The cook retires to the kitchen to bake a chocolate cake with the one word, "Welcome," on the frosting. Several of the men line up to have their beards trimmed and hair cut by whoever has taken on the duties of the base barber. And all pitch in with brooms, mops and dust rags to put the station in spick-and-span condition.

When the plane is reported thirty minutes out, all the men climb out of the station and walk to the skiway which they had prepared weeks before. Mostly they talk quietly and joke about signing up for another winter.

Then the plane appears, a speck in the sky, and the eleven men of Eights line up in a straight line. As the plane touches down they salute, tears streaming down their cheeks, welcoming the end of their long isolation and scientific vigil.

SEVEN

THOUGH the Americans have mechanized the Antarctic with Caterpillar Tractors, Weasels, Sno-Cats, Sprites and airplanes, the New Zealanders still depend upon the sturdy husky dog and sledge teams to carry out their field traverses and scientific explorations. The New Zealanders (known as "Kiwis" after their national bird) are based at Scott Station, just three miles over a hill from McMurdo. There is a close bond between the two stations, and the men of both installations often visit one another, winter and summer alike.

According to the Kiwis, the Americans are overmechanized. The New Zealanders feel that their dogs can go places tractors fear to tread. Furthermore, they maintain that dogs rarely break down and when they do, no spare parts are needed, just rest and tender loving care. Most of the territory the New Zealanders are exploring is the Ross Dependency, in which one third of all the exposed rock and mountains thus far discovered in the Antarctic is located, and only dogs seem to be able to get around efficiently in this area.

The dogs were reintroduced to the Antarctic in 1957 by Sir Edmund Hillary. Since then, the original kennel of twenty-four dogs has grown to seventy, all bred on the antarctic continent. The dogs are a cross between malamutes from Alaska and Siberian and Greenland huskies. Since the breeding of the dogs in the Antarctic has been done scientifically, the New Zealand dog handlers are convinced they have developed an animal peculiar to the Antarctic. Except for the first few weeks after birth, the New Zealand huskies live their entire lives out-of-doors, both summer and winter. During the winter, shelters are built for the dogs, but they prefer to "nest" in the snow, curling up into tight balls of fur to be drifted over by raging blizzards. The dogs, which may be tawny brown, off-white, black or spotted, grow to an average shoulder height of about thirty inches. Their life span is about eight years, and they rarely suffer any illness.

Antarctic huskies are strange beasts. They're friendly enough to humans, affectionate in fact, but among themselves, they're probably the meanest animals on earth. They fight, even in the traces, and the only way they can be separated is by the dog handlers' wading in among the snapping jaws and pulling the dogs apart. But on the trail, when the dogs are really going, they don't have time to fight. They seem to like nothing better than to pull the loaded sledges steadily, hour after hour.

The dog teams, made up of nine animals each, usually haul a twelve-hundred-pound load and average between eighteen and twenty-four miles a day, depending upon the terrain. Some teams have been known to make forty-five miles in one day. The dog team travels at a steady two or three miles an hour, and it is no

easy task for the two men who make up each sledge party to keep up with them.

One thing every Kiwi dog handler learns is that he mustn't display too much affection for any particular dog. When he pets one dog in the sledge traces, he must pet every other one in turn. Otherwise, the dogs, violently jealous of each other, will break out in a free-for-all that will require nine men, one for each dog, to break up. The training of the dogs is a long difficult business. Every day, for four hours a day, two dog handlers take out eight- or nine-month-old puppies, harness them to the traces of an empty sledge and set out, running all the way, one handler at the head of the dogs and the other at the sledge, teaching the huskies their tasks. . . . .

Each dog in the kennel is tried out as a possible lead dog. Few make the grade. The leader must be an obvious standout, for if the lead dog can't assert his authority over the other eight dogs in the team, the others in the traces behind him will run him down, jump him and maul him. Above all, the lead husky must be intelligent and quick to the orders of the sledge commanders. No whips are ever used to urge the dogs; all commands are verbal. These commands are a far cry from the simple old "Mush" of the Yukon days. In the Antarctic, orders to the dogs have been fitted to the pleasure of the animals. They're words which the dogs hear quickly, even in a howling wind, and to which they respond with amazing speed.

With the command, "Are you ready, boys?" the dogs stand up alert in their traces. They look back at the sledge commander behind the team and seem to be eagerly awaiting the next order, "Wheet!" which means "go."

"Wheet, boys, wheet, wheet, wheet," are words repeated over and over again as the team lurches forward in the traces, pulling the sledge across the snows. After an initial tugging, the sledge begins to slide easily and the dogs trot steadily across the snow-swept antarctic landscape. It is a beautiful sight.

To turn the dogs right, the command is "Auk," for a left turn,

"Rrrrrruck," with a rolled "r." To stop the team, a barely audible "Ahhh, boys, ahhh" brings the dogs to a slow panting halt and to immediate bickering among themselves.

The sledge used is of the Nansen design, a sledge that has been used in practically every known polar expedition, from the conquering of the Arctic to the attainment of the South Pole. It is made entirely of wood lashed together with rawhide so the vehicles will give with the terrain. The only improvement made over the years had been the plastic lamination of the sledge runners to prevent wear on the wood.

The sledge party routine in the field is an onerous one. Up at 7:00 A.M., the men breakfast, carry out scientific observations, break camp, stow their sledges, hitch up the dogs, and with a little luck, they are away by 10:00 A.M., for a steady, eight-hour, nonstop haul. The men never ride the sledge but ski alongside in a strange rolling glide which resembles a cross between ice and roller-skating. It takes months to perfect this skiing technique. A light snack is eaten on the move, and usually consists of buttered, enriched bread, a candy bar and hot coffee or tea, all of which are prepared at breakfast time. The sledge and dog teams halt only for scientific observations or sightings which, once taken, see the dog teams off again at even a faster pace to make up lost time.

The day's run usually ends at 6 P.M., earlier if a good camp site is found. The dogs are first taken from the traces and staked out far enough from each other to prevent them from fighting. Before taking their own supper, the men feed the animals. Fresh seal meat is carried for the dogs when the teams leave camp. After the seal meat is used up, the huskies are fed pemmican, an enriched meat. As dessert, each dog gets a dose of cod liver oil, which they adore.

After the dogs are fed, the men do their work, catch up on notes and observations, and then set about preparing their own meals, which are often quite elaborate. Every ten days or so, a plane from McMurdo will fly out to the field party and drop mail and fresh supplies by parachute. Radio contact with the main camp is maintained twice daily.

Traversing by tractor, while not nearly as romantic as exploring with dog teams, has the advantage of being a good deal less physically demanding and certainly more comfortable.

The usual American traverse party in the Antarctic is made up of eight men riding in three Sno-Cats. Specially designed to operate for great lengths of time in heavy snows, the Sno-Cat measures between fifteen and twenty-six feet in length, depending upon how it is altered for use. The body of the vehicle is suspended over four independent tractor treads. The diesel-powered Sno-Cat is between three and eleven tons, depending

A Sno-Cat at Byrd Station

upon size, and is divided in two sections—the cab for driving, and the living quarters, behind the cab, where the two or three men sleep.

All the vehicles are painted orange—the best color for spotting in the polar area—so they will be visible at great distances in the snow. Each of the tractors traditionally flies a pennant from its long whiplike radio antenna. The lead Sno-Cat, however, always carries the Stars and Stripes.

On an average traverse, two Sno--Cats haul a large rolligon trailer—a flatbed built on four over-large rubber tires, each inflated with five hundred gallons of diesel fuel for the vehicles' engines. The flatbed of the rolligon is loaded with the food and scientific gear, as well as spare parts for the vehicles. The third Sno-Cat in the traverse hauls a hutlike sledge called a wannigan, which measures eight feet by eight feet by six feet. An insulated building, this is the mobile kitchen, dining area, scientific laboratory, and recreation center for the men on the traverse.

Traverses in the Antarctic are made only in the summer when the weather moderates and the sun is up. The trips are carefully planned and so thoroughly worked out that almost every situation is anticipated in the time schedule, from delays caused by bad weather to breakdowns of the vehicles.

In the field, the mechanized traverse party is supplied with food, mail, fuel and spare parts by air every two weeks. Radio contact between the men in the field and their base headquarters is made twice a day—in the morning before the day's run begins, and at night, when the three Sno-Cats curl up for the evening. In these radio reports, the party leader advises base headquarters of his exact location, condition of the men and machines, status of his supplies and any interesting events or discoveries of the day.

Though an antarctic traverse may sound like romantic adventure, it isn't. Driving the Sno-Cats across the uncharted plains of the antarctic desert on extended trips is cold, uncomfortable hard work. The temperature in the tractor cab rarely rises above 35° F. The men are forced to sit in tight, cramped quarters and the special stoves installed in the back of the vehicles are little help in keeping the men comfortable when they stop for the night.

While driving, constant watch must be maintained for crevasses and landmarks. The weather must be checked regularly so that the vehicles will not be separated by a sudden blizzard. Radio contact between the three Sno-Cats is constant, and this, compounded by the noise of the engines, is nerve-racking. Within days of setting out, every man's face is lined, and set in a perpetual squint from sun glare.

As the Sno-Cats chug off after breaking camp, they proceed single file, spread out over a distance of several miles. There are two reasons for this method of travel—safety and science.

The lead Sno-Cat is equipped with a special crevasse-detection device to protect it and the following Sno-Cats from inadvertently tumbling into a crevasse. A crevasse is a deep gash in the ice which cannot be seen because it is covered over by a soft bridge of drifted snow. It is perhaps the greatest danger a traverse party faces. Some of these are thousands of feet deep and, just as often, hundreds of yards wide.

The crevasse detector on the lead vehicle is made up of four fifteen-foot poles extending like a fan from the front of the tractor. Between the four poles are three aluminum pans which ride on the surface of the snow and are linked to an alarm in the Sno-Cat's cab. In effect, the crevasse detector is a radar device that detects hollows and crevasses in the snow before the tractor does and alerts the driver, through the alarm, to dangers ahead. A good idea in theory, the crevasse detector in practice is not the best method of making a traverse through a crevasse area. When such an area is encountered, a member of the expedition ropes himself to the lead Sno-Cat and moves off about one hundred feet ahead. With a long metal rod, he probes the surface of the snow to determine whether or not the snow

is solid enough to carry the weight of the vehicles. It may be a slow way to travel, but it is safe and sure.

The second reason the traverse party travels as three teams spread out over several miles is to aid in scientific observations. Seismographic soundings, for example, must be computed between three points. When a sounding is made by setting off a blast of dynamite in the snow, the shock waves which ricochet off the solid ground thousands of feet beneath the snow can be read from three different places simultaneously. Thus the contour and depth of the ground below the ice can be measured with absolute accuracy. The spread-out travel technique also allows the last vehicle leaving camp in the morning (and the first vehicle stopping for the night) to carry out additional work, such as digging pits for glaciology studies, taking gravity readings, and working out the charting of the area just covered.

The tractors make a maximum of thirty-six miles per fifteen-hour day provided, of course, that they don't break down under the pressure of such extended driving. Usually they do break down, so the average distance covered is about twenty-five miles a day—about the same distance covered by dog teams.

As the Sno-Cats move across the area under exploration, marker flags are put every few miles so the party can, if necessary, retrace its treads with a minimum of navigational computation. Also, in case of emergency in which search planes are grounded for extended lengths of time, a rescue party could reach the distressed traverse by following the markers. In the course of the day, there are frequent halts for examination of the snow and ice by the glacier experts and for readings of the gravitational pull in the area. Seismographic shots are made at least once a day.

Lunch is eaten on the move as on the dog-sledge expeditions, but sometimes hot food is prepared the night before and carried on a small shelf extending, from inside the Sno-Cat cab, over the engine, to keep it warm. More often than not, however, the tractor traverse parties content themselves with candy bars, bread, peanut butter, and gallons of coffee kept warm in a Thermos jug carried between the driver and his assistant.

Depending upon the length of the traverse, the men pause every third day for twenty-four hours of thorough scientific study and observation. This includes drilling thirty or forty feet into the ice cap for snow cores which are studied for stratification, temperature, radioactivity and minerals. Seismographic readings are made over a fifteen-mile radius of the base camp while the traverse meteorologist makes a full hour-by-hour record of the weather, winds and temperature at the site where they are laying over. Meanwhile, the men assigned to look after the tractors give them a careful check and repair any worn parts which may have developed during the preceding seventy-two hours on the trail.

The men look forward to these twenty-four-hour halts, for they provide a brief respite from the incessant jolting and bucking. The layover also gives them a chance to recover from the constant headaches caused by the noise and fumes from the Sno-Cat engines. Three good hot meals, well prepared and served, add to the comforts of the rest period. But the high spot of the layover is a "trail shower."

Its ingredients are simple: a bucket of steaming hot water; a large, warm, dry towel; a wooden box to stand on; a moderate temperature of, say, $-15°$ F., a calm wind, and nerve. Before each trail shower, the men lay wagers as to the length of time each man will take. Then the bather strips off his clothes in the traverse wannigan, grabs the bucket of hot water and dashes out into the cold to the wooden box. He jumps on top of the box, pours the bucket of scalding water over his head, and dries himself as quickly as possible to prevent the water from freezing on his body. Then he zips, as quickly as he came, back to the comparative warmth of the wannigan and a fresh change of clothes. The whole shower takes about thirty seconds but antarctic legend has it that one man on a traverse from Byrd Station got through his shower in seventeen seconds flat.

Meals on the move are much more elaborate than might be imagined. Breakfasts are hearty, consisting of fruit juice, scrambled dehydrated eggs, bacon, bread and butter, and coffee.

The night meal is usually a generous helping of steak, potatoes, canned vegetables, tinned fruits and a choice of coffee, tea, or cocoa. Soup is always available. One man is usually designated as cook for the entire traverse, and this is his only duty the whole trip. Cooking on a traverse, though, is as exhausting as the driving, which is shared by all the other men.

When heavy weather, such as a blizzard or a white-out, sets in, the traverse men cease all operations and park their vehicles and sledges, covered-wagon style, in a small tight circle. During this spare time, the men busy themselves catching up on notes and scientific work, and relax by playing bridge, cribbage or chess, writing letters, reading, or joining in for a roaring hootenanny or an argumentative bull session.

As one seasoned explorer put it, "Life on these traverses becomes pretty elemental. Simple pleasures are enough for the men. The isolation of the polar plateau makes the sound of one's own voice bearable; what is more, it makes it sound good. Once we start talking, there's no stopping the discussions—science, politics, religion, the Antarctic...anything just to hear ourselves talk." The scientist looked off over the snows for a moment. Then, turning back to the interviewer, said, "There's no question life on a traverse is difficult; it's hell. But the ability to make the best of it depends upon each man's sense of humor, strength, ability to get on with every other member of the party, and belief in what he's doing and why he's down here."

On the trail, mirages are common because of the glare of the sun on the snow and on the millions of ice crystals in the air, which act like prisms, often refracting scenery forty miles away. Though often bothersome, these wispy bits of ice drifting in the air are a treat to the men on an extended expedition. The millions of ice crystals, driven by the wind, often reflect the sunlight like silvery needles and put on a colorful display resembling a daylight aurora, and reflecting every color of the spectrum. Often haloes form around the sun and sometimes two or three suns seem to beat down on the travelers. This is caused by ice fog—dense clouds of ice crystals high up in the sky, which cause the sun to appear as a mirage in different parts of the heavens.

Generally, however, every day on a traverse is like the day before —hours of crunching and rocking over hummocks of snow in an unrelieved white blankness. Two miles an hour, hour after hour they go, with only brief pauses, until about 10 P.M., when the day's run is finished. Then the men clamber out of their tractors to prepare a base for the night. Supper is at midnight. A cigarette or a pipe, some talk about the day, then yawns and the men turn in for their sleeping bags and a brief but deep six-hour sleep in the glittering sunlight of the antarctic summer night.

Depending upon the area to be explored and the thoroughness of the studies to be made, traverses last between one and four months. All the men are volunteers and scientists and most of them are very young. The traverses are usually sponsored by universities under grants from the United States Antarctic Research Program under the National Science Foundation. They are, of course, supported and supplied by the United States Navy.

Many persons often ask why, with the increased use of airplanes, traverses are still needed. They are slow, inefficient and highly dangerous. The answer is simple. Only a traverse can establish the true nature of the area being explored. It is all very well to fly over an area and get a general overall picture of it, but for complete information, there is no substitute for detailed on-the-ground plotting of the ice cap and sounding of the ground below.

Man is in the Antarctic to find out the hows and whys of the continent. The only way to do that is for man himself to tread the continent with his own two feet, aided of course, by four paws or steel treads.

EIGHT

THERE'S A club in the Antarctic that sooner or later claims all explorers, naturalists excepted, as members. The club, which issues a distinctive button to each member, is called "The I Hate Penguins Association." The reasons for membership are readily apparent to anyone who spends any length of time among penguins.

"Penguins are stupid" is a saying often heard around bases bordering penguin rookeries. And, despite their loud protestations of loathing for the two-foot-high, black-backed, white-breasted, flightless Adélies, the men devote virtually all their spare time to the curious sport of penguin-watching.

One scientist based at the now closed Hallett Station, which was located in the middle of an Adélie rookery, put it this way, "I hate those silly birds. I can't stand them. They're stupid. They don't make sense. But here I am staring at them for hours on end just as I did the last time I was down here. They hold a fatal fascination for me." He sighed. "While Hallett was still operating, during the winter, when the birds were gone and the men exhausted everything there was to talk about, they turned to penguins and penguin stories. Then, when summer returned, the men began penguin-watching again, staring at them in hopes of getting a fresh fund of tales to tell."

How do you become a first-class penguin-watcher? First you must learn to get near the bird so that it won't run away, honk at you or take a bite out of your leg. Actually, you must learn to approach the penguin so that it thinks you're just another penguin. That, the veteran penguin-watcher will tell you, is an example of how stupid the penguin can be. The idea is to get as close to the bird as possible and just stand staring at it. The penguin just stands there staring back at you. This is the height of refined penguin-watching. However, the Adélie's attention span is limited and within a matter of minutes, or even seconds, the bird will either nod off to sleep, start singing to its mate, pecking at passing penguins, or go waddling off around the rookery to no particular purpose whatsoever.

For any installation located close to a penguin rookery, the most important precaution to be taken, aside from care about fire, is the locking of all doors to billets. Navy Lieutenant Eldon Fitch, the base commandant of Hallett Station during 1962-63, tells of one harrowing Sunday afternoon. "I was sleeping in my quarters. For some reason, I stirred with uneasiness to wake with a start and find seven smelly Adélies standing, side by side, the length of my bed, blinking and staring at me. I must have been snoring and attracted them in from outside through a door accidentally left open.

"The birds looked at me with that vacant expression of theirs which somehow seemed to say, 'How is it that you're in our nest even though we've never seen a nest like this before?' I think they decided my quarters would make a good roost. Well, there was nothing I could do but try and shoo the birds out of the building. I called for help, and four of us took an hour rounding up the seven Adélies. You know, the only way you can catch and hold a penguin is by tackling him, grabbing him by the legs, and carrying him, upside-down. Those birds went skittering hither, thither, and yon—croaking and pecking and beating us with their flippers. We were certainly a bunch of bruised men when we finished clearing them out of the building. As for the billets, they were a complete wreck."

Summertime for any station near a rookery is a bedlam of constant gurgling and squabbling among the birds. They'll be quiet for a few minutes, then a mass hysteria will sweep the rookery and the birds will go wild, screaming and pecking at one another and running willy-nilly around the rocks, destroying nests, bowling over chicks and flapping their wings in defiance

at one another. And, just as quickly, they will calm down again.

There are two types of penguin in the Antarctic. The most common is the Adélie, first seen by Dumont d'Urville in 1840 and named by him for his wife. These birds are considered the clowns of the continent. They are of medium height, standing about twenty-four to twenty-six inches high, have a glistening blue-black back, a yellowish-white chest, a reddish-orange beak, and yellow eyes with black pupils. Sometimes, it is said, if you

Adélie penguin rookery about forty miles from McMurdo

look at an Adélie's eyes long enough, they will appear square rather than round. It breeds on solid ground in rock-strewn rookeries during the summer. In the winter, the bird disappears. No one knows where.

Two outstanding features of an Adélie rookery are the noise and the smell. The Adélies can be heard for miles. And the smell is overpowering in this otherwise odorless land. The sound this penguin makes has to be heard to be fully appreciated. Rearing back its head, it waves its flippers slowly back and forth, emitting all the while a low pulsating sound, which gradually slides up scale to an earsplitting, reverberating climax which sounds like a strangled gurgle with tremolo.

The second species of antarctic penguin is the emperor, an even more mysterious bird than the Adélie. The emperor stands about thirty-six to forty inches in height and is regarded by ornithologists as the most primitive bird alive. Unlike the Adélie, the emperor breeds and lives entirely on the ice. It breeds in winter, and during the summer drifts out to sea with the pack ice. It doesn't nest, but incubates its eggs by keeping them atop its webbed feet under the folds of its stomach for warmth. Only five rookeries of emperors are known to man.

Actually, much more is known about the Adélie than about the emperor because the antarctic winter has proven too forbidding for scientific observation of the latter's mating and incubating habits. It is known, however, that emperor penguins crowd around in huge circles, like football huddles, keeping as close as possible, with their backs to the wind as a means of keeping warm during the winter and incubating periods.

Both birds are fantastic swimmers. Though flightless, their wings become flippers in the water and the penguins literally fly in the water as they swoop after small fish and krill, a two-inch, shrimp-like crustacean. Both species are diving birds, capable of leaping into the sea from heights of ten and twelve feet. With equal ease, they can leap the same distance out of the water back onto the top of the pack ice. To make these leaps, the penguins swim deep into the water and then, gathering speed, like a stone from a slingshot, they catapult themselves out of the water to plop on the edge of the ice pack above the water. Sometimes Adélies, after swimming and fishing in formation, will leap out of the water and set themselves down, side by side in rapid succession, on top of the ice. Then they'll waddle off to the rookery, a hundred or so yards from the water's edge, to feed the young, take over the incubating of new eggs, or to quarrel among themselves.

Except for skua birds, which prey upon penguin eggs and young chicks, and leopard seals, which lurk in the waters near the penguin rookeries, the Adélies have no natural enemies. Because of so few enemies through the ages, the penguin is almost tame in its wildness and is absolutely insatiable in its curiosity. The penguin cannot run very quickly, but, when pursued, it falls over on its belly and, using its flippers and legs, propels itself on its belly across the snow and ice towards the water's edge, easily outdistancing any of its pursuers except the skuas.

Penguins mate for life. Recently it has been discovered that the birds identify one another by the sound of their trilling voices, which accounts for the tremendous noise that so characterizes an Adélie rookery. Since all the birds and their nests look alike, the penguin, to find its mate, goes from nest to nest bowing to the bird at the nest and trilling its love call. If the penguin picks the wrong nest, it is pecked for its serenade, and must totter off to yet another nest, crooning his identification song. When the right mate is discovered, there follows a long period of bowing, crooning and flipper flapping.

It was once believed that male penguins collected stones for the nest, dropping these stones at the feet of the female as a love offering. This theory has been proved wrong by Dr. Richard Lee Penney, a young naturalist who has spent years in the Antarctic studying the Adélie and its habits. He said, "Both sexes among the Adélies share in stone gathering and in the building of the nest. The sex of Adélie Penguins simply cannot be established by following the common misconception that the male penguin presents stones to the female." All the birds spend every spare moment running around the rookery stealing stones from one another. This aspect of penguin life gives the rookeries their appearance of constant frenzy and movement and explains the continual fighting that goes on among the birds.

Adélie penguins have amazing homing instincts. Even after long separations over great distances, the penguins are able to find their mates and return to their former nests or home rookeries. In an experiment made in 1959, five Adélies were flown twenty-four hundred miles from their home rookery, tagged and marked, then released in the middle of the Antarctic on a flat, featureless plain. Though it was believed that penguins do not travel during the antarctic night, ten months after their release three of the birds were found to have returned to their original rookery, nests and mates. They had covered the entire distance, averaging eight miles a day.

During the summer months, penguins feed very well, and the history of the Antarctic is dotted with stories of the birds being used as emergency food by stranded sealers and ill-fated expeditions. Once, in the late 1800s, the German Antarctic Expedition led by Professor Erich von Drygalski aboard the *Gauss*, was beset by the ice and forced to winter in the Antarctic. They soon ran short of coal, but Drygalski, remembering that they were stranded close to an Adélie rookery, resorted to burning the fat, oil-rich blubber-coated penguins as fuel for his ship's engines through the winter.

Adélie penguins lay two eggs a season, hatching them on dry ground in their stone nests. During incubation, the male and female penguins take turns at nest relief during the thirty-four days it takes to hatch the egg. While one penguin keeps the egg warm, the other mate feeds for several days, returning to take over the nest while the other bird feeds. But 68 per cent of chicks that hatch do not live; skuas feed on eggs and chicks, or the parents wander off and abandon the chicks. This is a matter of great concern to naturalists who believe the Adélie, and possibly also the emperor penguin, is nearing extinction.

The emperor penguin—one of the few animals known to man that rarely, if ever, set foot on land—locates its rookery on the pack ice close to shore. It lays only one egg per season, breeding solely during the antarctic night in the bitterest cold. As summer approaches, the emperors make their way north to the pack ice and the sea, not to be seen again until the sun begins to set for the winter. Nobody knows where either species of penguin goes —emperors in summer or Adélies in winter—or what they do once they leave the rookeries after breeding. Both species, however, have been seen hundreds of miles from the antarctic coast, adrift atop ice floes, just standing around penguin-style, gawking, and quarreling among themselves.

The skua, which preys on young penguins, is the scavenger of the Antarctic. It is a large, fierce, fearless bird, gray tipped with black, with a hooked beak and gull-like wings. It soars and swoops like a hawk, perches like a gull and, according to some, can be trained to come when whistled for. It establishes its colonies near penguin rookeries and various scientific stations around the Antarctic. This remarkable bird has a tremendous migratory range, flying as far north as South America during the antarctic winter, and ranging to within two hundred miles of the South Pole in the summer. Usually, however, the skua lives close to the antarctic shoreline, where there is always a plentiful supply of food.

The only other forms of animal life native to the Antarctic are the whales and seals which abound in the surrounding waters. These oceans, in fact, are so rich with aquatic life—krill and plankton, the food of the whales and the seals—the seas are often as thick as pea soup.

Two types of whales are common to antarctic waters: the blue whale, which has great commercial worth; and the killer whale, which has no marketable value whatsoever. The blue whale is the largest mammal on earth. It grows to an average of 150 tons and has been hunted for centuries for its oil-rich blubber and carcass; even its bones have commercial value.

Aside from man, the blue whale's chief enemy is the killer whale, called the "wolf of the sea" because it travels in packs. Considered the most vicious and sinister animal in antarctic waters, the killer whale will even attack shadows cast on the ice above the water. In attacking these shadows, the killer whale dives deep, then, gaining momentum, crashes against the ice above, shattering up to two or three feet of ice thickness in an attempt to spill whatever is casting the shadow into the water.

The killer whale grows about thirty feet long and has a shark-like dorsal fin rising about five feet out of the water when the animal swims near the surface. The killer is also distinguished by its speed, small beady eyes, hooked snout, and habit of rising vertically out of the water, porpoise fashion, to look out over the pack ice in hopes of discovering a careless penguin too near the edge of the ice. It has been reported that killer whales have actually thrown themselves onto the pack ice to attack penguins and human beings. The U.S. Navy especially cautions its personnel to keep a sharp eye for killer whales when working anywhere near the water's edge.

The penguin has become the symbol of the Antarctic and the whale is today its one economic asset, but the history of the Antarctic has been intimately bound up with the seal. There are now only three known species of seal in the Antarctic. Before the era of the great commercial seal hunts of the 1800s, however, there were probably many others. The most numerous yet least known of all the seals in the Antarctic is the crabeater. Less than a dozen have ever been observed closely, yet it is known that thousands upon thousands of them live on the drifting ice floes surrounding the continent. They rarely migrate close to shore. At best guess, they grow six feet long and weigh about five hundred pounds. They are known to breed only in winter.

The Weddell seal is the only antarctic seal that lives along

the shores of the continent. A friendly animal, the Weddell is completely undisturbed by the presence of man and only gives a curious look—barely raising its head in greeting—at anyone that comes up to it. One Weddell, affectionately called Lucille, used to hang out around the pack ice pressure ridges near Scott Base, three miles from McMurdo. Lucille followed the men around, watching them as they carried out their scientific work or trained their dog teams. The Weddell seal grows between eight and ten feet long from nose to tail flipper, and averages about nine hundred pounds when fully grown. Since the Weddell has no commercial value as a fur animal, it was never hunted, which explains its great abundance along the antarctic coasts.

When temperatures drop to the —70°s during the winter, the Weddell abandons the ice for the water, where the ocean temperature never gets colder than —28° F., comfortably warm to a Weddell. Since the seal is a mammal, it must come up for air every fifteen or twenty minutes. This means breathing holes in the ice must be kept open throughout the chilling winter. The Weddell's teeth are specially adapted for sawing holes, for air or escape, in the eight- to ten-foot thick pack ice. A Weddell carving an air hole in the ice is rather like a beaver attacking a tree—ice chips fly in all directions as the seal chomps his way through.

There is much about the Weddell seal to interest zoologists. It is, for instance, the coldest of living mammals and yet is able to maintain a body temperature equal to that of man while it swims in the icy Antarctic waters or rests on the continent shore in subzero weather. It is able to dive to depths of fifteen hundred feet under a pressure of seven hundred pounds per square inch. It has a complex signaling system with which it is known to communicate while underwater. It is also believed to use a sonar or radarlike system to find food in the murky antarctic waters, and to find air holes during the darkness of winter.

Scientists have recently begun recording the underwater

Above: *Weddell seal and pup*
Below: *Swabbing seal's mouth to find bacteria*
Right: *Webbed nets are used to transport seals without injury.*

sounds of Weddell seals near their rookeries. The noise can only be described as something like tuning in on thirty radio programs at once. The waters resound with gurglings, bubblings, thumps, high-pitched whines, snorts and hums, all of which travel great distances in the water.

Unlike the seals we're accustomed to seeing in zoos or aquariums (which are, in fact, sea lions, not seals), antarctic seals have tiny flippers. While graceful and swift in water, the seals of Antarctica are barely able to move their great bulks when they are ashore. When they do move, they undulate forward in a slow, wormlike, squirming fashion. They are generally peaceful but, when angry, they can break a man's leg with a whiplike

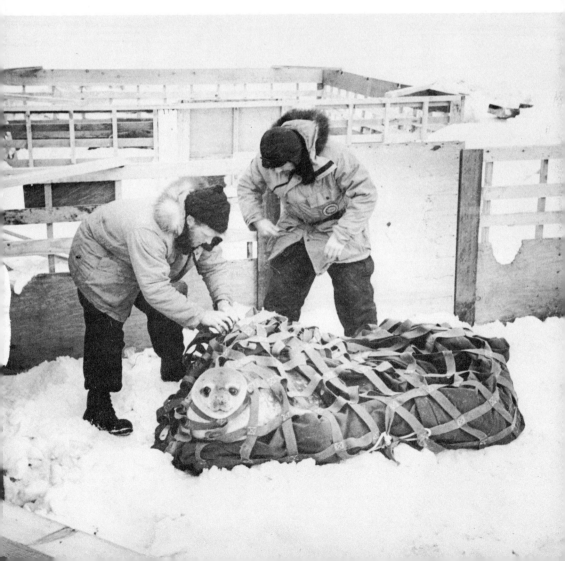

motion of their flippers, which they flail about from side to side or beat up and down, all the while snapping their powerful jaws with such speed that their teeth chatter like a machine gun going full blast.

During a recent expedition, the New York Zoological Society brought back some Weddell seals for study at its New York Aquarium in Coney Island. Research is now being conducted at the aquarium to determine how these seals adapt to the more temperate climate, and the effects of the climate on their physical system.

The third antarctic seal, the sea leopard, rivals the killer whale for meanness. It is a spotted seal with a long neck and a serpent-like head. Like the Weddell, the sea leopard is clumsy on land, but in the water it is as nimble as a watchspring and has been known to leap a full ten feet out of the water to snatch at a penguin waddling too close to the pack ice edge. Unlike the Weddell or crabeater seals, the sea leopard is predatory, feeding on fish and flesh alike. Though little is known about the sea leopard, it is a fearless animal, and there are many reports of this seal's chasing and attacking small boats. Like the crabeater, the sea leopard breeds during the winter on the pack ice far from the coast, but it swims close to shore to feed on penguins, its favorite food.

Except for the penguins, the seals, the skuas, whales and man, and the dogs and Manchurian ponies he brought to the Antarctic in previous expeditions, this land of frozen time knows no other warm-blooded life. But who knows what life this once sub-tropical continent did support? Some geologists are convinced that the Antarctic was once roamed by dinosaurs. But proof of this must await the day that man is able to dig down beneath eight thousand feet of snow to the buried land below.

NINE

IN A rather obscure museum in Istanbul, Turkey, all but crowded out of sight by other exhibits, is displayed a magnificently hand-colored, gazelle-skin chart which has confounded experts on the Antarctic ever since the map was called to their attention. Incorporating details from other charts, some dating back three centuries before Christ, the map was drawn in 1513 by a Turkish admiral, Piri Reis, who made a hobby of collecting and drawing maps.

The reason this particular chart by Reis has baffled antarctic specialists is simple; it shows, comparatively accurately, the coastline of Antarctica as it is supposed to have appeared five thousand years ago. This coastline, as shown in the Reis map, is ice-free and dotted with ships.

Is it possible that the antarctic coastline was indeed free of ice and known to man as recently as a mere five thousand years ago? Or is this map merely the coincidental concoction of a fanciful cartographer? No one really knows, nor for that matter, is willing to venture a guess. The reason is that a second mystery involving the Antarctic remains to be explained.

In 1893, Captain C. A. Larsen, a Norwegian whaler, while anchored off Seymour Island on the tip of the Antarctic Peninsula, discovered fifty clay balls set on pillars made of the same material. Captain Larsen, a respected authority on the Antarctic, reported, "These (balls of clay) had every appearance of having been made by human hands." If this is true, Captain Larsen's discovery places primitive man farther south than ever previously imagined. Are these clay balls man-made? If so, how old are they? And how did they get to Seymour Island in the Antarctic? Who put them there? What were they for? But all of Antarctica is mystery—a great unknown. And because it is unknown, man is there.

Man is a curious animal. He must know everything there is to know, whether the knowledge has a practical use or not. Except in the realm of pure science, the Antarctic at this moment is useless to humanity as a commerical enterprise. If there is any economic potential in this frozen wasteland, it certainly lies decades before us.

No doubt, great mineral wealth lies somewhere in this frozen white desert. Dr. Laurence Gould—scientist, geologist, educator, adventurer, and one of America's great antarctic explorers—claims, "Antarctica remains one of the few great economic resources left in the world. I'll stake my life on it, there are tremendous natural resources on this continent from which all humanity can gain. The only economic drawback to developing these resources is costs versus profits. The costs would certainly be exorbitant—in the beginning."

What has been discovered has been encouraging—gold, tin, silver, platinum, molybdenum, antimony, traces of oil, unbelievable quantities of coal, some seams thirteen feet thick—sixteen minerals so far. Obviously it is but a question of burrowing down through the ice cap and tapping these resources once the lodes are discovered.

There's no doubt man can survive and live in this cruel cold continent. This has been proven. The successful operation in recent years of McMurdo's nuclear power plant gives evidence that atomic energy indeed holds the key to man's eventually

Field camp in the Taylor Dry Valleys

turning the great Antarctic waste into at least a partially habitable place—certainly a place to see and visit.

Many well-informed travel experts agree. Voit Gilmore, former director of the United States Travel Service, a branch of the U.S. Department of Commerce, feels there is a great tourist attraction in the Antarctic, if not for the winter sports enthusiast, then certainly for the traveler seeking something different and offbeat. One South American airline, in fact, holds a future franchise for tourist flights between Buenos Aires, Argentina, and "some-place" in Antarctica, whenever such flights become possible.

It has been suggested in all seriousness that plastic-covered settlements could be established at one of the more spectacular spots on the continent—Hallett, for example—hotels built, and atomic-energy-heated swimming pools installed. Imagine swimming in subzero weather with ten-thousand-foot-high mountains jutting straight up from poolside and penguins press-ing their beaks against the plastic dome. Far fetched? Stranger things have already happened in just the last five years.

If tourism is an economic potential for Antarctica, it will de-pend heavily upon conquering the problem of transportation. Here, too, national governments, travel experts and airlines have a vital interest.

The southern hemispheric lands of Australia, South America and Africa are anxious to find an aerial shortcut which would link their continents together, eliminating the long, tedious, and costly routes across Asia, the Pacific and Atlantic Oceans. (The north polar flights have already become a short-cut between northern Europe and the West Coast of the United States.) This necessarily depends upon the establishment of accurate weather stations and emergency landing places, and the development of airplanes with long enough range and the ability to withstand the awesome cold that would be en-countered in such south polar flights.

In September 1963, Rear Admiral James Reedy, com-mander of Operation Deep Freeze '64, led a flight of U.S. Navy planes from Capetown, South Africa across Antarctica and the South Pole to McMurdo Station and then on to Christchurch, New Zealand. Normally such an air trip would take thirty-five hours and involve a flight of 13,705 miles. Via the South Pole and Antarctic, the flight took twenty-two and a half hours and covered seventy-one hundred miles. This flight, perhaps the last pioneer flying exploit in aviation his-tory, proved finally that a south polar route connecting

Australasia to Africa was not only possible, but a very definite thing of the future.

What of Antarctica today?

Today, this continent is the last great natural scientific laboratory on earth. There should be no question of "Why is man struggling to know and understand this lost continent?" He must. In the Antarctic, man can come closer to understanding our earth and perhaps space beyond.

Space scientists carefully go over the physicists' studies to determine what effect the lines of magnetic force will have on future rocket launchings of vehicles and men from earth into space. Meteorologists chart and examine the antarctic weather to find some pattern to its behavior, and to determine what effect the weather originating in the Antarctic has on the rest of the world.

Above all, science is anxious to learn more about the history of earth, and perhaps a clue as to how the earth was formed and the continents and oceans created. All this may lie beneath the frozen continent's snows.

Antarctica is a wasteland. It is also one of man's best hopes.

For years, many nations have claimed territory in this forbidding place. National pride, prestige and hope of gain have driven many countries to take a part of Antarctica as national territory and set up specific governmental departments for administration of this territory. Two nations have almost gone to war over which one owned a useless, snow-covered bump of land located in the Weddell Sea. By common consent among all the early exploring nations in the Antarctic, a large portion of Antarctica, in Marie Byrd Land, has been set aside—reserved —among the nations claiming land in the Antarctic, against the day the United States may seek sovereign domain in the seventh continent. But the United States has spurned all official claims to antarctic territory, believing that nations should be free to do peacefully whatever they want, wherever they want, whenever they want in this immense ice-capped expanse.

There is no question that the political wranglings and activity of the past—the finders-keepers drive of centuries ago—are now over. Antarctica, thanks to science and the International Geophysical Year, has given birth to a great international agreement —the Treaty of Antarctica.

By the terms of this treaty, all military and economic problems, and all territorial claims in the Antarctic and connected with the continent, are set aside for a period of thirty years. In other words, twelve nations of the world—Argentina, Australia, Belgium, Chile, France, Great Britain, Japan, New Zealand, Norway, the Soviet Union, the Union of South Africa, and the United States—have designated Antarctica as international territory.

Since the pact was ratified in 1961, these nations have repeatedly joined in sending expeditions throughout the continent seeking the truth of science. Competition between nations has been eliminated for the time being. There have been

no clashes worth recording; angry words at times, but no fights.

Except for survival-equipment requirements, there are no weapons whatsoever in over 5,100,000 square miles of snow. Firearms have been banned by the Treaty of Antarctica and this clause has been respected. International inspections of various bases in the Antarctic were carried out for the first time in 1964, to see whether the terms of the Treaty of Antarctica were being strictly adhered to. The inspections proved they were.

Perhaps this dread land is providing the stage upon which the nations of the world will learn to work together in harmony in all their endeavors.

Perhaps, then, it isn't so much science that counts in the future of Antarctica and the world as the fact that twelve nations have agreed to abandon force in at least one part of our planet, reserving that territory to peaceful pursuits so man may better understand himself and his world.

INDEX